MASTER PIECE SEX

The Art of Sexual Discovery

Elaine Kittredge

Illustrated by Stephen Hamilton
Foreword by Lonny Myers, M.D.

Published by

P.O. Box 10378 Chicago, IL 60610-0378

All drawings are artist conceptions. Any resemblance
to actual persons is purely coincidental.

Published by

P.O. Box 10378
Chicago, IL 60610-0378

ISBN 0-9611266-3-9

10 9 8 7 6 5 4 3 2 1

Sex is an erotic painting on the canvas of the spirit.

Table of Contents

Foreword vi
Preface 1
Sex, Guilt and Politics 7
Sex as a Mirror 15
Sexual Repression, Fear and Guilt 21
The Virgin and the Whore 29
The God and Goddess 35
STDs and Fear of AIDS 45
Sex as Your Own Garden 57
Flirting 65
Erotic Kissing 73
Using Your Hands and Skin 79
Touching and Hugging 85
The Five Senses–Especially Sight 93
Orgasmic Masturbation 99
Fellatio as a Master Stroke 105
What Do Women Like? 117
Giving a Woman Oral Sex 127
Fantasies and Phone Sex 135
Magic Beyond Space and Time 143
A Miracle Occurs 149
In Closing 153
Erotic Love Poems 157

Foreword

Far from being raised in a sexually accepting household, Elaine Kittredge was brought up by a strict, anti-sex mother who, insisting she was masturbating, beat her with a strap during her sensitive pre-adolescent years. The truth is that she was scratching her genitals because of an ongoing undiagnosed yeast infection. Some would call this good religious training taken too far. After all, the Vatican still considers masturbation as a 'seriously disordered act,' thereby giving parents righteous authority to punish children for masturbating. Most sexologists and psychologists today consider such punishment child abuse. Sharing this and other sensitive personal experiences of her sexual life, Elaine includes just the right amount of autobiographical material throughout the book, enough to keep the reader aware of her personal involvement without straying from the main purpose of the book: to speed up and enhance the learning process of adventuresome sex, the process of squeezing every sensuous drop from the deep well of our potential.

Her aggregate of information, which comes from serious study of Western and Far Eastern philosophers including their outlook on sexual eroticism, combined with her other studies and personal experiences, has equipped Elaine with a deep understanding of the sensual/sexual aspects of our humanness. Her writing is down to earth, comes straight from the heart, is poetic and pleasantly erotic.

She remains especially interested in the ideas expressed by various Far Eastern philosophers who emphasize the flow of life's pulses, the ability to let go of the intellectual, the need of using both hemispheres of the brain simultaneously rather than in a linear fashion. She is particularly enthusiastic about the body-mind connection in healing and well being as expressed currently by Deepak Chopra, M.D.

The idea of a spiritual connection in sexual erotic stimulation is in direct opposition to the Patriarchal Judeo-Christian dualism of good versus evil. I personally liken this fundamentalist Christian attitude toward sex to our generally accepted attitude toward killing our fellow human beings. Killing is inherently evil, deserving of harsh punishment, except during war and self-defense, when it becomes good and is rewarded. Similarly the fundamentalist version is that sex is evil, deserving of harsh punishment, and becomes good only in marriage, and, for some, only when the purpose of the sexual activity is to conceive children.

Although Elaine does not dwell on homosexual experiences, she expresses total acceptance of such relationships. Regarding STDs (sexually transmitted diseases), she wavers between accepting the need for protection, and describing sexual activities with a freedom and spontaneity that seems to preclude the use of condoms. It is my personal medical opinion that the danger of contracting STDs among health-oriented adults who avoid anal sex has been exaggerated both by the Centers for Disease Control and the media. By 'health-oriented' I mean persons who are relatively well nourished; take care of their bodies with cleanliness and exercise; avoid sex when they are ill; avoid sex when they have a discharge and/or have any lesions in the genital area; abstain from drugs and have a low alcohol intake. Any sexually active person can get an STD, true. It is also true that the hysterical news coverage about herpes in the seventies and AIDS in the nineties directed at the low-risk group I just described is more a means of scaring people into abstinence than a true description of risk.

The U.S. Department of Public Health (USDPH) and the Centers for Disease Control have never been eager to promote the prevention of STDs. I worked in STD public health clinics for ten years and was not allowed to promote the use of condoms until after the outbreak of AIDS. Postcoital disinfection, a method of STD prevention highly successful in WWI, WWII, Korea and Vietnam, has never been promoted in this country for civilians.

Back in the 1930s it was known that the ingredient in many commonly used contraceptive jellies and creams, namely non-oxynol-9, killed the organisms that cause gonorrhea and syphilis *in vitro, i.e.,* in laboratory experiments. When I heard this in 1971, I was furious. I organized a conference on STD prevention. The experts all agreed it was true: vaginal contraceptives, used properly, would reduce the risk of STD transmission. Reporters from radio, television and newspapers were present and heard the facts. It was a long night. I impatiently waited for dramatic headlines and newscasts revealing the good news to sexually active women all over the country. It didn't happen. The reason given me was, "We do not want the public to know; it would give women a false sense of security." I was horrified both at the control the 'powers that be' had over news coverage and the absurd reason offered by officials from the USDPH. Are the media possibly exaggerating the facts on the spread of AIDS in healthy, heterosexual individuals in order to prevent a 'false sense of security' and also to make headlines? I'm not saying they are, but I wonder.

Again, this was my personal experience and is not the purview of this book. Elaine believes merely that people are entitled to the truth so they can make their own decisions regarding protection, choice of partners and specific activities.

Regarding spirituality being ultimately connected to our sexuality, Bagwan Shree Rajneesh is one of the few modern religious leaders who believes that sexuality is essential to spirituality. He writes: "Never repress it [sex]! Never be against it. Rather, go deep into it with great clarity, with great love. Go like an explorer. Search all the nooks and corners of your sexuality, and you will be surprised and enriched and benefited. Knowing your sexuality, one day you will stumble upon your spirituality. Then you will become free. The future will have a totally different vision of sex. It will be more fun, more joy, more friendship, more a play than a serious affair, as it has been in the past. Sex is just the beginning, not the end. But if you miss the beginning, you will miss the end also."*

Elaine weaves threads of spirituality throughout her book. Along with Bagwan, Stan Dale and others, she concludes that much of true sex education consists of unlearning the inappropriate fearful messages we were given as children and young adults, and disregarding many of the negative messages that continue to bombard us. Although the book is full of wondrous hints and suggestions at how to enhance sexual enjoyment, the concept that is clear throughout is that one does not have to learn about sex, but rather to increase body awareness and allow the sensual/sexual needs of one's body to surface and gently solicit attention.

In our society we reward curiosity, creativity, and proficiency in almost every field of human endeavor—except sexuality.

Elaine speaks from both the female and male point of view, but there is a not-so-subtle emphasis on the feminine aspects of eroticism. This does not make the book less appropriate for men. In fact it may well enhance the male reader's enjoyment.

The sensual drawings by Steve Hamilton and the activities Elaine describes come alive, producing for some readers vivid memories and for others delicious fantasies. Some readers may, as I did, often think: "That's true—that is what good sex feels like.

*The Association of Sex, Nov./Dec. 1983, Vol. 2, No. 5

That is what I want in a good sexual experience. Sex *should* be a joyous celebration!"

Another message in the book is to start *now*. Don't let precious moments, days, years go by before the perfect situation arises. Learn from others; experiment. She does not offer any hints as to how to find a partner with whom to enjoy body-to-body contact, but that is not within the realm of this beautiful book.

Rather than a sex manual, Elaine is far more erotic, describing the silky sensations of gentle body contact and the roaring excitement of sexual gusto. The descriptions of specific sensual/sexual acts are never separated from the totality of the person, the totality of a meaningful, rewarding experience. She recognizes the skin to be the greatest, most sensual organ we possess. Implied, but not stated explicitly, is to experience eroticism within the limits of responsibility and respect for other persons.

Her descriptions of the various sensual/sexual experiences depict ultimate, total, exotic ecstasy. Such experiences occur, but the reader should not be discouraged when such magnitude of energy, physical pleasure and spirituality does not occur. Enjoy the book for what the title states—Masterpiece. Even the best artists do not create a masterpiece every time!

Lonny Myers, M.D.
Member, American College of Sexologists

Preface

I wrote this book for everyone who wants to be a better lover, and I wrote it in a personal way that you will enjoy and relate to.

I wrote it for my daughter, and all other young people who need validation of their sexual identities. Although I wrote it for my daughter, it was a great risk for me to give the manuscript to her. She is a very incisive person, and I knew she would be totally honest. I was afraid of revealing myself to her so completely as a woman. It seemed inappropriate as a mother, and yet it was a way of my sharing in a non-threatening way my own life, especially my sexual history and philosophy. Fortunately for me she was not particularly shocked, and she liked what I wrote. I was quite relieved and grateful, and I grew from taking the risk.

I wrote it for myself. I never had anyone teach me personally or from books what I eventually learned over the years from experience. I never found the sex book I was looking for, so I decided to write it. I wondered why a person should take a lifetime of experience and not share it, so I decided I would. Why is sex considered shameful unless it is properly laundered by puritanical religious ideas and the politics of a controlling society? Why should really good sex, in all of its myriad aspects, be considered wrong or sinful? As if only boring one-dimensional sex is holy, but creative and magnificent multi-faceted sex is evil. Why should talking about sex or making a double-entendre draw comments like "Get your mind out of the gutter" as though sex were some kind of refuse?

I wrote it for adults who believe they have the answers and because writing makes me think and grow. I wrote it for couples to read together so they can begin an open dialogue about their own sex life to discuss openly and safely things that otherwise might feel too threatening to their relationship.

My male friends who read the manuscript thought it was

geared more toward women, and a feminist publisher thought it was oriented more toward pleasing men. This alone was a sign that I had reached a happy medium. Couples who read the book said it helped create a freer sexual expression in their relationship, and found the book opened a new door to realizing their sensuality and understanding and accepting it. The manuscript was read by heterosexuals, gay men and lesbian women, couples, singles, young and mature. I tried to write it without prejudice. But I do have a woman's eyes, and I am heterosexual. The book cannot be complete or total, nor should it be. It is my own personal processing of all the books I've ever read, all the experiences I've ever had, and the experiences of those persons I've known who have verbally shared pieces of their private lives or experiences with me. It is probably best read together, if you are a couple, for that will open a door to the room of understanding, where it is safe to discuss all problems and desires without fear or judgment.

In short, this book is for everyone.

Regarding my personal beliefs about sexuality, I don't think it is wrong to be sensual and sensually aware in or out of bed. We have a divine gift called sex, which is creative in limitless ways. I believe expressing your sexuality fully is necessary for complete growth and knowledge of yourself. Learning your sexuality *is* learning yourself—your beliefs, your hangups, and your poetry. It is my opinion that every belief you have ever had will show up in your sex life, *e.g.*, your willingness or unwillingness to trust, etc. How open you can be sexually will indicate how much you are willing to trust your lover—not control your lover so that he or she will have to walk on eggshells in order that your tender and vulnerable sexual belief system will never be challenged. Letting go of your ego and expressing your feelings both verbally and non-verbally will allow you to learn that you are in the artist's chair in your painting of life, and what you believe, you will most surely paint. The gallery can be as large or as small as you wish, include monotonous or colorful works. It's all up to you, the artist. You can paint spontaneously and freely or buy the paint-by-number set and stay within the lines using only colors that have been premixed. Life is long enough and patient enough to teach each lesson without rushing. Learning can be a very enjoyable experience when we drop our prematurely chosen defense systems, our rigid, fearful attitudes, and our imagined boundaries.

This is one woman's need to share her journey so that possibly you can save a few years in your own journey to becoming a better lover. Perhaps you can know and enjoy yourself earlier in life than I did. Maybe you can reflect, at my risk to share, what your own self is holding and withholding in life's great adventure. For if we don't consider life an adventure, it may become an ordeal. Even boredom is an ordeal. I believe your view of life will prove itself at every turn. In other words, your attitude of life will reflect itself in all you choose to see and will color your view of your experiences. Everything you see is a reflection of your self, so learn from your mirrors—your friends, your job, your lover, and all your life situations. They are your problems or your teachers. Life loves you beyond belief. Now it's your opportunity to embrace life in return. Your ability to accept your sexuality without fear and shame will give you the ability to make love to your problems in your embrace with life as well.

Sex is a grand expression of the artistry of life. In my mind's quest, when I asked my deeper self, "What is sex?", the answer came without pause: "Sex is an erotic painting on the canvas of the spirit." I encourage you to enjoy life's expression. Paint your lovely paintings as a gift of spirit. Combine your spiritual self with your physical self in the profound expression, the playful and delightful expression, the passionate expression of your sexual paintings.

I send you blessings of delight at your discovery of yourself and your lover in your life's adventure as expressed in the playfully erotic and profoundly spiritual paintings of your sex life.

Sex, Guilt and Politics

There is a secret older people need to share with the young. Because it is a seeming contradiction to Judeo-Christian morality, it is the kind of secret you keep even from yourself. This is the worst kind, because a secret like this involves such deep shame the psyche is afraid to acknowledge it.

The reason for our shame is due to the distorted but official view of morality. Because of our belief that sex is basically shameful, if not downright evil, the innocent self is confused. And even that confusion is kept secret. We are secretly ashamed of our natural need for sexuality. We are confused and frightened by its all-consuming power, rather than experiencing it with awe in an innocent and mystical way. What soul can describe accurately the depth and power of sexual orgasm? By refusing to look at our fear- and shame-based attitudes, we cannot possibly see the sexual/spiritual connection, and we therefore can never integrate the spirituality of our experience because we cannot recognize it.

Lust is considered one of the seven deadly sins. It is forgiven if a legitimate child comes forth. It is officially scorned if experienced for pleasure. Now, what rot. If one can deny the intense goodness of orgasm, there is an obvious denial, and consequential lying about reality. An essential human need is scorned and made ashamed of, instead of being acknowledged with gratefulness. Since one who believes this also believes God is commanding this shame, there is a contradiction in creation. This view of sex is shame based and is an extremely limited interpretation of sexuality. If we believe in a creative deity, how then can we deign to define, explain or limit the meaning of all creations of that deity?

Moralists will pound their fists. However, even they cannot deny the intense awareness of bliss with orgasm. It is a bliss that goes beyond the body into a spiritual awareness.

The saddest thing of all is that any experience seen through the eyes of guilt will preclude what I believe is the natural and spontaneous physical healing produced in the body which emanates *throughout every cell* just before, during and after orgasm. I believe orgasm is healing, but the healing will be aborted if there is guilt. I believe orgasm is the most innocent act a human being can experience because it is total and uncontrolled surrender to one's humanness. The desire for it can be distorted, and the choice of partner can be fallible, but the human act itself is neutral of any judgment. Deepak Chopra, M.D., has asserted that during any positive exhilarating experience, Interleuken II floods the body. Interleuken II is a powerful anticancer neuropeptide, the body's chemical equivalent to the feeling of joy.

Why has sexuality/sensuality been relegated to the sin pile? I offer a theory that the reason is essentially political in nature. Wilhelm Reich wrote a book called *The Function of the Orgasm.* He wrote another called *The Mass Psychology of Fascism.*

The book on the function of the orgasm elaborates on the healing and release of all body energy blocking. It is a must for any therapist, and not bad reading for the lay person.

The book on fascism describes the personality developed by those who block their sexuality. Fascism is not necessarily only a philosophy with Hitlerian overtones. Fascism is a fear of freedom—a belief that a free person is a dangerous person, especially if that person is female. The secret evil (sex) must be controlled. So it is evident. Sexual people must be repressed. Or at least sex must be repressed. A free person enjoys sex, and that is a threat to society (the *id* of Freud is dangerous) because that person is uncontrolled.

Our belief in political freedom contradicts our fear of personal freedom. Consequently, our entire culture lives a contradiction. We profess to believe in freedom, while we repress ourselves internally. In actuality, we are afraid of our freedom. Our sexuality is the most apparent example.

I am not speaking about sexuality as an addiction. An addiction is something that prevents us from discovering ourselves. Sensuality and lust in sex are not *per se* addictions. They can become addictions in a fearfully compulsive person. But lust and sensuality in sex are not equatable to addictions in a healthy person. In other words, lust and sensuality are not intrinsically bad, just as money and power are not intrinsically evil. All can be misused, but they are not in themselves evil.

The human desire for orgasm should not be judged unkindly or scorned. For example, our shame of our need for sex is what makes us embarrassed when we want to talk with someone to whom we're sexually attracted. Haven't you noticed how easy it is to be yourself and talk animatedly with someone who doesn't turn you on? Yet I'm sure you've also noticed that when you get in a room with someone to whom you're sexually attracted, you freeze and can't seem to speak or look at that person? This can change, and I hope it will during the course of reading this book. The basis for such embarrassment is the shame you feel for a human need. Human needs should not create shame. Sexual shame is a lie that pervades society based on the lie that a free (sexual) person is dangerous and evil, wanton, and a user of others.

I believe this attitude is the origin of the need for control. Society will control utimately (force). The church will control in a secondary manner (fear masquerading as morals). And what neither of these can reach, the trained psyche of self will control (guilt). This is an acceptable form of mind control. Your locked-in sexuality becomes your biggest shame. But the basis of that shame is a lie. This lie swirls around at the murky bottom of one's need to control others, but especially the need to control oneself. This need to control based on fear and shame destroys creative thought and action. It is the antithesis of freedom. We don't live in a paradox, which would be acceptable. We live in a lie. We live in a fearful society that encourages control rather than freedom. We talk freedom but we do not live in freedom, because fear and freedom cannot coexist. The ultimate control mechanism society uses is guilt. And it's inexpensive, if not free. Sex becomes the bogeyman.

There was a hue and cry back in the sixties when reforming educators propounded that our educational system was askew regarding human needs and human values. John Holt, A.S. Neill, and others came up with ideas that were revolutionary in humanizing the educational system. The traditional educators accused these men of encouraging license. But actually they were going against the moral grain in showing that children are basically self-regulating by nature. That, in fact, acting out is a reaction to being repressed rather than permission to express. The whole concept of original sin precludes the goodness and innocence of even a newborn. However, in the Judeo-Christian tradition permeating our society, this contradicts God, who is supposed to have created us in God's own image.

By believing in our innocence, in our innocent sexuality, the healing power of orgasm, the spirituality of sex, and the human gift of self-expression through sexuality, we are accepting our creativity and our birthright. We are accepting our sexuality as a gift not to be scorned. We are accepting life. We are accepting that sex is goodness and spirituality in its deepest sense, and that sex is given by our Creator for our enjoyment, our healing, and our spiritual completion as well as for our procreation.

This is the secret, as I see it: The more spiritual we become, the more sexuality pervades our consciousness. Not merely the sexual act, but the sexuality of the universe and the aliveness of the 100% activated sensual physical body. A spiritual person is intensely aware of the deeply sexual nature of his being and the universe. And the more spiritual a person becomes, the more sexually aware that person becomes. I'm obviously not speaking of sexual desecration which is basically anger in disguise. True sex is a sacred act. The ultimate sexual act is spiritual, and the ultimate spiritual act is sexual. This is a paradox, not a contradiction. In spite of society's segregating the two, they are, in fact, universally congruent.

Sexuality is an expression of abundance and overflowing, a cornucopia, a celebration, and an acceptance of oneself, the other, and life as experienced in all of creation. We are the mini big bang experience of the universe, creating energy in our abundant explosion.

Define your own sexuality. Do not be intimidated by the prejudices of your society.

MASTER
PIECE
SEX
15

Sex as a Mirror

Sex on a purely honest level will teach you who you are.

The way you express yourself sexually mirrors who you are. Are you timid? Are you expressive? Do you risk making movements or sounds that are out of the ordinary for you? Do you make noises that are squeaky or animalistic? Can you look into your lover's eyes with total openness and abandon, or do you look away? Do you expand sexually, or do you contract sexually? Do you use your partner instead of your spirit to expand into wholeness? Do you use sex as a control or manipulation? Do you make love when you want to? Do you make love when you don't want to? Why don't you want to?

It is important to be honest with yourself. You will never grow if you deceive yourself. If you hide from who you are and what you want out of life, you can't grow. And if you aren't clear about what you want in life, no one else can be clear about it either.

I heard the other day that the only difference between a rut and a grave is the depth of the excavation. That's a groaner. You are the one to get yourself out of the rut. Not your partner, not your boss, not your luck. You. When you point your finger, there are three left pointing back at you. Self-honesty is the key to all growth. If you think your sex life is boring, you are probably boring. If you think your sex life is listless, you are likely listless. Once you can be open with yourself, you can be open with your partner. Not blaming. Remember, there is no blame. True honesty is not blaming, it is sharing. It is talking about your needs. There is no shame in needing. No one is an island. Being ashamed of our needs makes us stubborn, proud jerks. We don't need to do that to ourselves or others. Speaking through love, guided by gentleness and speaking our needs, without demanding, will strengthen a relationship. If there really is nothing left, and requests for sexual contact are continually ignored, then possibly you should end it. However, any relationship will be made better with openness. Remember, the only day you have is today. Don't lie to yourself today. You are a good person, and all that fear you have inside can dissolve each day if you are true to yourself.

The shame of our need for sexuality causes us to sublimate. Do you eat instead? Well, if you're overweight, that's good protection against sex. It makes the act quite physically difficult even with desire. Don't be ashamed if this fits you. Be willing. Be willing to be honest. You can lose the weight–that's not the problem. The problem is you are trying to lose *yourself.* Instead of wanting to run away from who you are, you need to accept yourself. All those negative voices that screech evil messages about not being good enough or beautiful enough can be reprogrammed. You *are* good enough–intrinsically, and without even changing. You *are* lovable. One affirmation that is quite healing in accepting your sexuality is simply, "I am lovable and sexy." Therapy is a wonderful tool if you feel stuck. Don't be ashamed to seek help if you need it.

The big problem in feeling bad is, if you have these yucky feelings all the time, you probably get pleasure out of stirring the pot. I had those feelings even *not* being overweight. I just felt inadequate. Not as good as. When I realized that these feelings were a habit, it helped me. Even though the feelings felt bad, they were familiar. But why should bad feelings have felt safer than good feelings? Because bad feelings were familiar. I was internalizing parental messages, and mama was always right. Feeling good went against the rules my family taught me. Feeling good scared me.

One trick in being kind to yourself is to be kind to others. The only trick to not judging yourself is to not judge others (including your children). This is very simple and very healing. But I assure you, judging is so engrained in us by the culture we live in, seeming an inalienable right and duty, especially as a parent, we really have to work to get rid of it. However, when you finally stop judging others, about anything, you will be free. It is a freedom of spirit you cannot believe until you feel it. It is quite possible, but you are going to be tenacious about holding onto your right to judge others. It really takes work. Letting go of being judgmental for the reason of condemning is worth every effort it continually takes.

It's okay to judge yourself if you are assessing. This is true for your life only. You have no business assessing others unless your entering some kind of relationship with them. Judgment is more condemning, more like, "You're boring, and you'll always be boring." Assessing yourself honestly includes accepting yourself as lovable and worthy even with the qualities you'd like to outgrow, like being boring.

Are you stingy sexually? Are you generous? There is a wierd thing we were taught as children. If you want something, hang on to it. Actually, the opposite is true. If you want something, let go. There is a flow with everything. Hanging on prevents the flow. This is especially true with energy. It is my belief that pain is caused from holding on, which blocks energy. Holding on is a form of control. Energy needs to flow like water. Water becomes stagnant when it doesn't move. So does energy. If you use your head like a cork on your body, your back muscles jam up. Loose jaw and throat muscles are the key to a relaxed back. When I put my hands on a friend's shoulders to loosen his back muscles, I can feel not only tension, but an unwillingness to let go. I say, "Let go of the pain. You don't need to hold onto pain. Let it out with your breath. Put it into your breath and breathe it out. You don't need it any more. Pretend you're a straw and let the energy flow in and out of you just like you are hollow. Or, imagine a fountain flowing out of the top of your head and the water is beautiful, radiant colors. Energy is an interesting thing. The more you let go of it, the more of it you get. Picture a clenched fist. What can you hold in a clenched fist? What can you say through a clenched jaw? Aren't you willing to let go? What can't you let go of? Asking yourself questions like this will teach you how to grow. Sometimes when we are little our households are so crazy that we control everything possible so we can feel safe. These controls start to strangle us when we get older, and only then do we feel pain from all the blocks we have built. Blocks built from emotional pain are the hardest to release. Shallow breathing and holding our breath is the quickest way to block emotional pain. But it blocks every other feeling as well, including good feelings.

Body blocking prevents energy from flowing naturally. Sexuality is only one avenue for human energy. It's bodily energy being channeled in a sexual way. It is the same energy that keeps your cells healthy, keeps your brain working. It is the energy of a healthy body. When you repress your energy, you begin to kill your body. Breathe deeper. Get those lungs full! Oxygen is fuel for your body. That energy is good. It is healing. And it is yours. An oxygen-deprived body is crying out to live. So let it live. Breathe deeply. Accept yourself for who you are. Accept your energy. Accept your sexuality, and don't be afraid of its power.

Sexual Repression, Fear and Guilt

Sexually repressed people usually feel inadequate. Although they don't show it, and may not be aware they feel 'less than,' the economy lives off their gnawing feelings of need. Buying products to revise their self-image is neccessary in order to validate themselves sexually, for validation is a sincere and healthy human need. But often, instead of being more creative and open with sexual expression, people usually keep their repressed feelings comfortably hidden from themselves, and instead purchase all manner of things to make them feel sexy: Expensive do's like hairdos and hair styling, hair coloring, salon pampering, etc. Hair is a symbol of sexuality, and if there's no lover to caress it, how wonderful to go to the salon where someone else will.

The caring and sensuality expressed by another's touching your hair is quite enjoyable. It can be an added joy to sensuality without its being a substitute. In other words, you might have free, joyous and even ribald sex quite often, and still enjoy having your hair done. But often, unfortunately, it is a substitute for the real thing.

Nails also seem to be a biggie for women. Nail salons became more prevalent in the late 80s since the 1950s' morality returned more due to the advent of AIDS than virginity worship. Perfect nails showing pampered hands. If you can't grow nails, you can always buy them. What a treat to have someone else play with your hands while you enjoy a long lunch hour getting primped. Again, there's nothing wrong with that, if it is an addition to your sex life rather than a replacement for it.

Make-up, facials, creams for the face and body. They are all wonderful enhancements and wonderful affirmations of your sexuality. But they also can be unsatisfying replacements when you'd rather have someone touching your breasts. There is nothing wrong with enjoying these happy and beautifying experiences. But these activities can effectively mask damaged self-esteem. It is important to look to the child within for any unhealthy messages that were foisted upon you as you were growing up. Reprogramming is the only true balm for sexual self-esteem damage—damage caused by fear around sexuality for masturbating, sex before marriage and the damage caused by incest. Much damage regarding sexuality was created by inordinate fear and guilt that was believed and used by your parents, and is still reinforced by society. Fear of disease, fear of pregnancy, fear of gossip. When fear of most diseases was eradicated by antibiotics, when fear of pregnancy was removed by the pill, we found other reasons to fear sex and diseases. Headlines are written to fear, and I believe statistics are possibly manipulated to endorse fear and encourage distrust of each other and our sexuality. Fear also leads to paranoia. There are sexual precautions available to avoid disease, which should eliminate paranoia. But even with these precautions many people remain paranoid and are leaning toward total abstinence as protection. People are afraid of kissing. The innocent kiss is being touted as the kiss of death. I suggest that when our fear turns to understanding, and our judgment and condemnation turn to compassion, we will build a world based on hope and health rather than fear and disease. I also suggest that the cure is truly in turning fear into love, and in turning our disease of hate and rejection of our sexuality into acceptance and joy. The only fears we are born with are the fear of falling and the fear of loud noises. All other fears are learned. Exaggerated fear is an imposter of the human condition. It is the only emotion that kills, quite literally. For fear is the beginning of emotional repression, and repression leads to feeling trapped. Feeling cornered or trapped leads to needing an out, and illness is the body's way of answering that need without emotional guilt.

Changing our life is the creative way of dealing with feeling trapped. I believe repression in all forms, including feeling trapped, is the beginning of most if not all illness. I am not speaking here of healthy responses of consideration which are spontaneous in-the-moment or moment-of-reflection forms of safety or self-chosen personal ethics. That is not guilt or repression, but consideration and choice of values. We always have choices, and are never really trapped. I am speaking against fear used as a moralizer, leveler, destroyer of spontaneity and killer of self-acceptance and self-esteem.

I grew up so frightened of sex that it is a miracle I survived. My mother beat me for what she thought was masturbating (and of course it hurt her more than it hurt me). I didn't even know what masturbation was. I had never had an orgasm. I happened to have had a yeast infection, which by her age, she should have experienced herself. I told her I itched so bad I couldn't stand it. She continued to beat me for having spots in my pajamas, so each morning, in terror, I would check my pajamas, and each night I would go to bed with heart-pounding fear. The beatings continued for at least a year. I was even beaten on Christmas morning when my new yellow soft pajamas showed my scratch marks. I couldn't control my physical body while asleep, so I finally started tying my hands with my robe sash, pinning the sash to the top of my bed. Now I am sure she must have known I was doing this. So each night I went to sleep with fear, and my bed was my prison. When I got older and finally did masturbate, to orgasm, I realized what I had been beaten for. Since it felt good, but I knew it was bad, I kept doing it, and kept feeling guilt, remorse and fear. But I had learned one thing for sure: orgasm was the biggest sin in the world. I finally decided the only way to stop was to swear to God I would never do it again. Well of course I did it again. But then I knew God would kill me for masturbating. I had broken an oath to God. God would kill me because of my sexuality.

Not only did this fear and pre-adolescent analysis destroy my ability to have an orgasm easily later on, destroying my sexual timing, so to speak, it put my adult self in an untenable, unrealistic dance with my sexuality. When I became a married adult, I had two tubular pregnancies six months apart, after having been on the pill. I was twenty-two years old. As I was being wheeled into the operating room, knowing on a cellular level that I was indeed dying, my subconscious belief was reconfirmed about God killing me for sex. I was not aware of this connection, of course. But it was there at the deepest level. When I returned to my hospital room, and was informed I would never have children, I cried and vowed to God I would never believe in Him even if He were there. I hated God, I hated myself, and I hated my sexuality which had robbed me of my right to motherhood. Below my consciousness I knew I was not worthy of being a mother because I was a secret pervert. I had masturbated and enjoyed it. The lack of adult logic in my subconscious decision, my feelings of worthlessness, and fear of punishment were all there. A child deep within, filled with torment, had translated my experience in that operating room into an example of God's punishment and the evil of my sexuality. The anti-sex God of my mother became my judge, jury and jailer. Fortunately I realized it before He became my killer. Now I realize, at that point in my life, I still believed sex was punishable by death—all, most dangerously, at a totally subconscious level.

These psychosexual wounds were raw for many years. Through therapy, reading, and love, they have surfaced and subsequently been healed. My distorted view of God evolved into a different kind of God—One that created sex rather than killed for it.

I'm sure you have your own wounds. They are secret blessings when used as learning experiences. Don't run away from them. Embrace them. They are your teachers. Love for yourself, realizing that you were created to be happy, joyous and free, and realizing that you have full inheritance of a boundless universe and universal love, can conquer any distorted belief system, and can heal any wound caused by a well-intended parent or priest. These wounds can serve as your liberators rather than your jailers and/or killers.

Support groups and group therapy are good because they take the shame out of secrets. God didn't try to kill me. My secret shame tried to kill me. To quote a well-known saying in a popular group, "We are only as sick as our secrets."

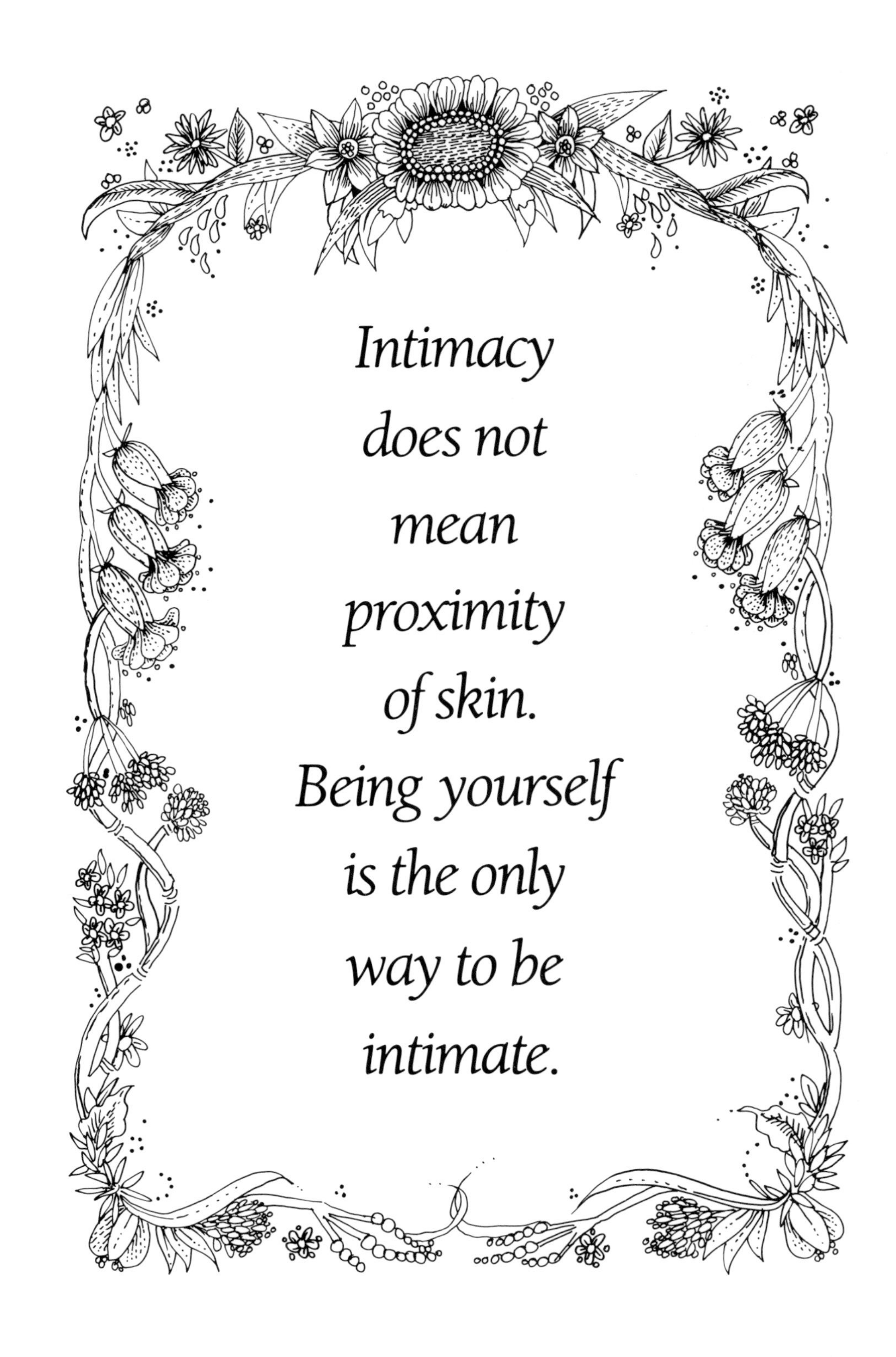

Intimacy
does not
mean
proximity
of skin.
Being yourself
is the only
way to be
intimate.

MASTER
PIECE
SEX
29

The Virgin and the Whore

Too often women are slotted regarding what men seem to consider experience. This appears to be an activity that men seem to enjoy. They don't seem to wonder what slot *they* might fit into if the roles were reversed. This unfortunately backfires on them. I heard the other day of a friend of a friend who, when she remarried after a time being single, pretended as though she were naive in bed. This she did specifically so her husband would not think she had been 'around' during the time she was single. I was aghast at hearing this, but when I thought about it, I realized she probably reads men much better than I. I am continually amazed that men think they teach women how to have sex.

It is totally erroneous for a man to think, if a woman is adept and comfortable in bed, she learned it from a man or men and has been 'around'. Sexuality is an inward journey. A woman teaches herself, first by knowing and loving her own body, then by trusting herself to allow herself to flow naturally in the arms and then into the thighs and genitals of her lover. Into his mouth, into his heart, into his soul and into his entire being.

A woman learns to be a good lover from her own heart and from the heart of her being. She does not need to learn it from a man. She learns it from her inner goddess.

You cannot even learn how to make love from reading books. Books will give you encouragement to be yourself. You might try different postures and positions, but you're better off trying a different mind-set. I read a lot of books because I'm curious. Especially reading about men's attitudes. I thought *The Hite Report on Male Sexuality* was fascinating. Since I've written this book you're holding in your hands, I become acquainted with David Ramsdale and Ellen Jo Dorfman who wrote a magnificent book called *Sexual Energy Ecstasy.* I highly recommend their book for further reading, because it is technique specific and offers wonderful information presented in a sensitive and poetically loving way.

It seems so sad to me that men limit women in their thinking to have caused this wife to give her husband less of herself out of fear of judgment. And she was probably right. He very possibly would have thought she'd been 'around'.

I've also heard women say, "Men don't like it if you know more than they do". "Men don't like it when women are better lovers than they are". A man I once dearly loved was intimidated by my having written this book because he was afraid I'd been 'around' and he might not be all the things I wrote about. He was afraid of how he'd stack up. Women don't compare as much as men seem to. For instance, men especially compare the size of their penis. However, you often hear women say it does not matter what size the penis is, but what a man does with it that counts, and all of the other things he does or will not do that makes him a wonderful lover or not. Enthusiasm and romantic attitude count much more to women than penis size. It's men who have given each other and themselves the hangup about size. Comparisons are so damaging, and you are your own victim when you compare. If you don't love your penis and you are not grateful for it just the way it is, especially when it is erect, that feeling will be picked up by the woman. Her embarrassment at your embarrassment might make her pay less attention to your penis because she feels your discomfort. Love it. She does. It's one of your finest gifts to her.

Women may possibly feel similar discomfort at the size of their breasts. How much does that detract from their sexuality to you as a man?

A freely flowing, loving woman is a joy in your life. Take her gift to you in the way it is intended, not wondering where she learned her flowing. She does not have 'wiles'. She is not, unless she is a gold digger, using wiles. Let her be creative in her love-making, not questioning where she learned it—not being paranoid of other men and her previous life situations of which you were not a part. People are not possessions, and every one of us has a history, which should be none of your business, anyway.

She is not a virgin or a whore, but a combination of innocence and virtue and passion and heated explosion. Accept this in its paradox. Allow yourself to accept your woman completely and love her passion as your own.

Nobody teaches you sex. Your sexuality evolves from your spirit.

The God and Goddess

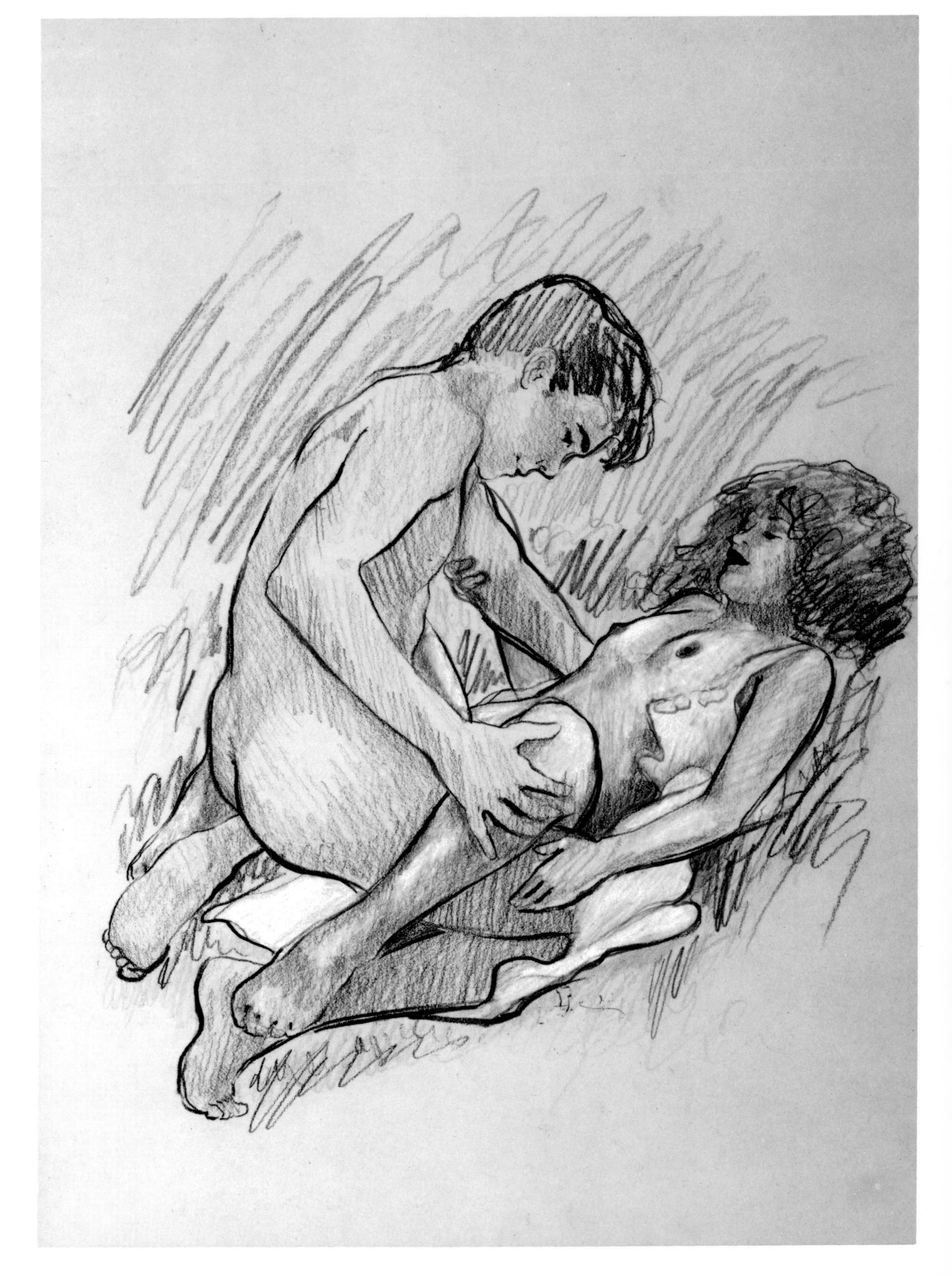

Pre-Patriarchial religions have always included sexuality in their rituals: Fertility rites of Spring, planting, and reaping the abundance of the earth as Goddess. These rituals were most likely on the various solstices, time markers of the ancient world. The Mother Goddess was worshipped well before the gods and goddesses of the Greeks and Romans and before the Semitic Patriarchal god. She was worshipped as the Earth Mother, who had given of her loving, abundant and fruitful body for her children. I have never read anything about the exact rituals. However, I believe when religion changed to a Patriarchal structure, rituals of sex were eliminated from all rites of religious celebration, suppressed, and probably even violently eliminated. The idea of lust was turned to sin, and the idea of group sex seen as deviant, immoral behavior. These ancient rites have been either ignored or eliminated from most current historical texts, but we are all faintly familiar with at least witch burning. What we call witchcraft is in fact an earth religion called wicca, stemming from the ancients, far removed from what we have been taught. Although I am not personally involved in any cult, including wicca, I can attest from what I do know that it is entirely harmless–in fact much more harmless than most favored religions. I can remember my own mother, in her self-righteous hatred, calling others 'pagan.' Paganism is an ancient religion connected with earth rites having nothing to do with evil or blood sacrifice. Paganism is often confused with Voodoo, which allegedly sacrifices animals, but that confusion is due to ignorance and prejudice in education. There is also a NuVoodoo, which is more philosophical in nature.

Paganism is actually a peaceful, non-invasive earth religion. I have a strong feeling that when the Patriarchal religions of the hunters took over the lands of the Matriarchal planters and shepherds, rape and pillage replaced fertility rites as a matrix for sexual expression, these being violent acts that were condoned, replacing healthy lust with dominative violence. Sexual orgies, so to speak, got a bad rap. Then, when the Patriarchal religious tribes cleaned up their rape and pillage act (unless you believe there were no rape and pillage during the Crusades or even current wars), rape or the condoning of it, was abandoned. It was still done, of course, but at least it wasn't sanctioned. Exciting, celebrative, lusty sex got replaced by sexual violence. Simply lustful human sex got a bad name as deviant. Rape became its violent descendent. Most sex on today's television is of a violent nature, and bloody murder is rampant and accepted as a form of entertainment, including what's reported on the news.

From what I know of mythology and history, and imagining what has been left out, these are just my educated hunches. But they do seem fairly logical in reviewing what we are told in today's history books and books on pre-history and mythology, and piecing together some of the obvious gaps. No one was bad or evil. It just was a change in consciousness. Patriarchy became a new paradigm. But sex, unfortunately, was the innocent victim. And, it's been repressed by religion ever since.

What one would hope to recapture from understanding all of this is the return of sacrament to sex: The holding of the sexual act as very special, awesome, inspiring, and an expression of gratefulness for an abundant universe. What we can perhaps glean even from the destructive acts of rape and pillage is that sex is animalistic, wild, and extremely powerful. Violence is a perversion of the power of sex. Violence is a contradiction of the sacred. So if we can combine both—the power and the sacred, eliminating the violence, we may be able to put more meaning and excitement back into an act which has been maligned and repressed throughout recent centuries. Claiming that good sex is non-lustful is to deny the awesome power behind it. Denial of the power is in conflict with all our animalistic desires. Human beings are wonderful animals. Sex is powerful. Orgasm is a powerful expression of the sacred and a sacred expression of power. It is our connection to the sexuality of the entire universe.

If we can use mythology to realign our identity with our sexual natures, we can truly benefit from the experience. I'd like to talk about some western sexual archetypes of both men and women, and why there is more than one archetype for each gender. Obviously Aphrodite (Venus) is the sensual female goddess. However, the complete woman will eventually identify with all of the other goddesses as well. Note, in passing, that Venus (female) is the root of the word 'venereal', which is usually used in a negative sense. Note also that Eros (male) is the root of the word 'erotic', which is usually positive in nature.

Here's a Greek myth that was likely a true story in some form. One day in a meadow, Persephone was enchanted by a flower of a hundred fragrant blossoms. But the flower was a trick, and when she got near enough to smell it, the earth below opened up. A great god (Hades) plucked her, instead, out of the meadow, and carried her to his kingdom (the Underworld). Instead of a scumbag grabbing her in the alley and dragging her off to his hole-in-the-wall apartment, or dragging her behind a bush or building in the alley, this guy became a hero because he arrived in a chariot of gold. Interesting. This sexual kidnapping theme (rape) runs through many mythology stories of many cultures. Sounds exciting, doesn't it? So long as it's a god in a chariot of gold. This guy sounds even better than the man on a white horse that all women wait for. A herd of pigs obliterated our little Persephone's footprints, and the pigs fell in too. (Here come the herds.) For a year after the abduction there were no crops. Mama was mad. And Mama was Demeter, the goddess of grain. Finally, Persephone was released, but not before having tasted of her shadow self. A nine-day ritual, called 'Thesmophoria', celebrating the sorrow of women over this abduction was later suppressed by the Patriarchal followers of the gods Zeus and Apollo. Abduction (rape) is a familiar theme in Greek myth, abhorred by the female goddesses yet enjoyed by male gods. The sun self, sacred, is frightened by the shadow self, profane. This is more Jungian. But we have to realize we each have both sides, so no one is good or bad. Each of us has a light and dark side.

Perhaps the excitment of sexual resistance by women, as they are pretending to fight off the abduction, is not to be ignored. Against one's will is more than criminal, it is evil. But perhaps excitement of the 'game' should not be ignored. Unfortunately, an unhappy result of this feigned resistance is date rape. It was believed that a woman was being merely coy to say 'no'. Today, however, she very likely means it. Beware. When I asked several men about this, they responded: "I always know when 'no' means 'no'."

The Greek goddess Athena is pure strength and wisdom. Most women in this new decade are enjoying a renewal of belief in their own strength, power and wisdom. This new destiny or paradigm is an enhancement of their sexuality rather than a negative value. A woman can be more assertive in bed as well as in the workplace. Keeping the sacred value of strength and wisdom enlivens a woman's sexual pleasure and the pleasure that she bestows.

The Greek goddess Hera, Zeus's wife, represents the strength a woman acquires with reaching middle life. Nowadays a woman is well aware that her sexual desire, prowess and strength increase with age. Her knowledge of sensual pleasure increases, as does her desire. Men have not totally accepted this, but the ones who do are the wiser. At middle age she is the virgin, the temptress, the whore and the wisdom of her sexuality all in one. Every stage she has ever lived through can be called upon.

The Goddess Diana, although beautiful, did not take well to men, especially the voyeur. She did many mean things, and her dislike of men's sexuality is embraced by many women in today's society. Some are celibate because of early sexual abuse and other reasons, while others are Lesbian. The myth behind the term 'Lesbian' is that on the Island of Lesbos women got sick and tired of the warlike antics of their men, so they kicked them all off the island. I would guess that male delight at watching two women have sex was behind Diana's punishing sprees, for there are few modern straight adult sex videos that do not include two women having sex. Never in straight videos, however, is a man touching another man. Men don't seem to think it weird or disgusting if women have sex together while they watch. Perhaps they think it's perverted only if it is not done for the viewing pleasure of a man. It strikes me as quite interesting that only one side is shown in sex videos. At least it is something to wonder about when analyzing human sexual behavior.

In this book I speak from a heterosexual viewpoint because that is my lifestyle. It does not mean I disapprove of homosexuality. I don't think there should be a judgment value on sexual preference or choice of partners.

Most popular and most identified with as a sexual goddess is Aphrodite. Her form, her grace, her sensual desire as well as desirability, and her haunting quality and undercurrent of passion for the sake of passion, make her easy for many women to identify with. She's my favorite, though I identify with all of them on occasion.

Note in passing, how the famous Greek statue of Aphrodite differs from today's mythic pinup, or Barbie Doll image. Today's model seems more the myth!

I enjoy identifying with the female goddesses. I once had an insight that changed my life. I was walking down the street feeling just great. It was early morning, my energy level was high, and I truly felt like the most beautiful woman in the whole world. I felt like the Goddess. When I realized this, I mentally said to myself, "I am the most beautiful woman in the world!" I then saw another woman, and said "and so is she" and saw another and repeated "and so is SHE!" I then realized that we are all the most beautiful woman in the world. We are all the Goddess in different forms at different times. My girlfriend still laughs joyously remembering my encouraging words one morning on a long-distance call, "Don't forget, Marie, you're Aphrodite's rep."

Women are probably more aware of their sacred form than are men. However, men also have their pantheon of gods with whom to relate. The current Men's Movement is awakening this quality for male participants. It is not just male bonding that occurs during ceremonial rites (weekend workshops), it is the connection to the sacred within each man. In classical Greek mythology, Zeus, of course, is the most powerful. Like Hera, he epitomizes strength and pure raw power. Wielding the thunderbolt, his penis, he breaks down all barriers to his strength and will, embodying the pure raw power of sex. Sexual kidnapping seems to be one of his favorite pastimes. Zeus once came to an abductee in a 'shower of gold'. I see this quite literally as his sacred sperm. Nowadays, a shower of gold has come to mean something quite unlike its original intention. He came to Leda as a swan (long neck), and pursued his human conquests in many guises and disguises. But men can always get a sense of power when they identify with Zeus energy.

Dionysos is the playboy of the gods. All men at certain stages or moments of their life long for the freedom and lustful abandon of this womanizing aspect of themselves. Unfortunately, he's got his flask which makes him an occasional jerk. But then, women are also occasional jerks.

Apollo, the god of strength, power, and wisdom, is a facet of men that makes them most enjoyable to women. The sparkling eyes of a bright, sensitive, aware man are an appeal beyond imagination. This is an aspect of men that is very sexual to women. He is the intelligence and brightness of man. I personally believe the deeper the man, the better the lover, and I don't mean a neuroticly self-centered intellectual.

Zeus and Apollo were also warrior gods. War has probably been a perverted form of sexuality for millennia. However, violence comes from repressed sexuality not expressed sexuality. When men make love they do not long to make war. A sexually satisfied society would be a more peaceful society.

The gods and the heroes are a living pantheon for men and women. They are colorful, zestful and wonderful expressions of each aspect of our figures, both physically and psychologically. My belief is that we should use these 'larger than life' beings to enrich our own self-appreciation. As we see ourselves as gods and goddesses, we reclaim that sacred rite of sex together as an act of incredible power and majesty, to bring the hugeness of the universe into our bedrooms, and into our female vulva and male lightning bolt penis projectile. To see the male organ with its glorious and frighteningly powerful attributes can add awe to our sexual awareness. For a woman, identifying the male with his godfigure is to accept the entire power of the male side of the universe as it enters our female goddess body. Seeing the female vulva as its heavenly powerful vortex of sexual delight should swoop every man into each radiant cell of his sexual body, driving him crazy with desire and passion.

A ritual of candles, incense and music is an added sacred touch. The woman's gift of cleansing the man and his cleansing her before and after the sexual act can add still another sacred quality to the rite. The sharing of a beverage from one goblet, massage and any small ritualized or spontaneous kindly gesture can bring the sacred and powerful into sex, and add to a beautiful beginning, action and closure.

Don't forget to keep the power of the sacred in your sexual act. Sex is not a sleeping pill. The sacred should always be invoked at least internally, before, during, and after sex.

STDs and Fear of AIDS

Fear is the number one debilitator of all creativity. I believe it is the major cause of illness. It is the cause of separation, discomfort and dis-ease. Yet we cannot ignore the fact that we must be careful with our precious bodies. We are worth protecting. But there is a thin line between being careful and paranoia.

Disease and guilt are interconnected in subtle ways. Guilt goes hand in bony hand with a belief in sin and punishment. And sexual issues have always lurked behind finger-wagging, frustrated men and women. Oftentimes the finger-waggers are the ones who beat and rape their own children and project their guilt onto others. Now, the children are coming out and telling their truths. The numbers are staggering.

The reason I bring this up is not to finger-wag back, but to show how anger and guilt destroy. It matters not which side of the fence anger and guilt fall. Damage lies in tying up one's energy instead of using it in a creative way. The only way to freedom is honesty and unedited grieving, which is easier said than done. New, easily available therapy groups and anonymous 12-step groups have arisen to fill the need. I believe they are effective whether or not they are professionally supervised. I recently had a therapist friend spew forth not-so-humble criticism of such groups and inner-child professional speakers. His theory was that you don't open someone up and then leave them with gaping wounds to go out into the world and possibly commit suicide. This is somewhat elitist thinking based on Freud's fear of the 'subconscious' being a bomb ready to explode. I don't believe we are so fragile, and a good cry goes a long way in releasing pent-up ancient emotion. Personally I approve of any non-professional co-counseling if it is not connected to groups that proselytize. There is also a thin line between grieving and self-pity. Self-pity is as damaging as resentment because it prevents us from taking positive action in our lives.

I believe not working through unresolved sexual abuse issues will be damaging to the mind and body, predisposing it to imperfect functioning. Many abused persons are buffered by excess weight in later years, likely as protection against further sexual contact. I believe we all have sexual abuse issues in some form, if only because society has such words as 'slut' for women who have more than one lover. There is no such corresponding abusive term for a male, unless he is gay. 'Womanizer' does not carry the same shameful innuendo. This single standard alone is a sexual abuse issue for all women and gay men, and there are many more such examples.

You can be 99% free of guilt, but that 1% will be just as damaging as if you were 100% guilt-ridden. The effect is worse, because you're unaware of the power of only 1%. In a psychology class I attended, guilt was defined as unexpressed resentment. In other words, when you feel guilty, what is it that you resent? Take note of that. Getting to the core of the issue is the issue. The solution to the problem lies in the meaning of the problem. Old resentments never die, they just fade from sight. Therapy means going back to your initial hurts and vulnerabilities. This emotional regressing and clearing will make you stronger and will free you so you can use your energy for more creative purposes. I even believe in such a thing as cradle rage—when you wanted to be picked up and were ignored. Sometimes the rage goes so far back it is pre-verbal. Honoring oneself means accepting these issues as valid and not stupid. All feelings are valid. We do not have to act on them all, but by recognizing them and crying the ancient cry, we dispel the power of the issue and free our energy up for positive action rather than negative reaction.

You may wonder what all this has to do with STDs and

AIDS. After all, these diseases are *real* and guilt, anger and fear are just feelings. And what does fear of sex and disease have to do with getting any of this stuff? You get disease from germs or viruses, not from feelings. Granted, the germs and viruses can be seen with a microscope, and fear cannot. Neither can the wind be seen, yet in cold climates we all are very cautious about the wind chill factor.

What I'm proposing here is that we attract what we fear. Our mind is so intensely focusing on what we fear that it acts as a magnet to fulfill what we're thinking about. And if we have ever-so-buried guilt, we believe in sin and punishment. Church and society contend that all sex out of wedlock is sinful. The corollary is that such action should be punished. Since we grew up in this society, and most of us have sex as singles, an eensie weensie part of us believes we should be punished. The finger-wagging 1%. So, that 1% sniffs the air and searches far and wide to locate the germ or virus to fulfill its deepseated belief in punishment. But of course, we can't see that. I am not saying that we should not use condoms if we are single and have sex. But even with condoms, we should look into our philosophy of thinking. The theory I believe is this: The universe does not believe in limits, and it seeks to give us what we want in a cooperative venture. However, since consciousness is non-judgmental, the only way the universe knows what we want is by what we think about. We are supposed to be the guardians of our thoughts for creative thinking. That's why we have to dredge our psyches. So then, the universe says to itself: That's what he's thinking about, it must be what he wants or he wouldn't be thinking about it so much, right? So if that's what he wants, let's put it in his life. If you think this sounds crazy, just put this in the back of your mind, and watch your life for a while. You'll be surprised.

I recently was the victim of my own fear, and it was a wonderful lesson in many ways. I had been dating a professor from a local university who has his Ph.D. in psychology. I met him at a party, and although I noticed he drank more than he should, his personality fascinated me. Before the end of the party, he asked for my phone number. So far so good. Except I ignored the fact that he drank excessively, and that wasn't good.

He called me the following Wednesday, and we started to see one another. When it came time for sexual moves, he made them, and I did not object because I was quite attracted to him. But we did not use a condom. After all, he had his Ph.D., a nice condo (please add the 'm' next time) an incredible amount of charisma, and he was no mental slouch. Just my kind of guy. When he found out I drank only mineral water, he bought several varieties. He co-authored a textbook. And he was very affectionate. He said all the right things, and even if they were lies, I liked hearing them. I knew they were lies, but they were nice ones. Poetic. Every man should be poetic, and he most certainly was just that. And besides that, he really excited me. He communicated well, was fun, humorous and oh-so-very sexy. So far so good (but remember I did not put the 'm' on the condo).

We saw each other for several months, and suddenly I started to see something else too—a discharge. They now have a cute name: STDs. But they're not so cute when you find them. I freaked out for a moment, then called to make a doctor's appointment. Not only did his poetry include trichomonas, but his repertoire extended to chlamydia as well—two STDs that men pass on to women, in ignorance, because they themselves may not have symptoms.

Well, I wasn't angry. It was sex with consenting adults. I could have said 'no' to no condom. But I was not cautious. After all, who wants to use a condom besides the manufacturer? Professor went away for Christmas, so I had to use the mail to let him know. Again, I was not angry, but to be sexually responsible, we both had to take the necessary medications. So I dropped him a letter.

Then, as I started to think about it, I realized that in order to truly be sexually responsible, I needed to get an AIDS test, respecting the three-month window.

Now I started to scare myself, especially since I had time to wait and stew. You don't get an AIDS test unless you think you might have it. I could tell myself I was being sexually responsible (after having been sexually irresponsible), but the fact still remained. If I got two infections from Herr Professor, maybe his sexual contacts had been extensive enough to include contact with the dreaded 'A'-word. I decided to go with the Department of Health and get a free, anonymous test. Calling for the appointment was fearful for me. Again, any admission of need for testing seemed like a death sentence for myself and anyone I had touched. I felt defiled and ashamed and felt like there was something innately horrible and wrong with me. They were very nice and non-threatening on the other end of the phone, and told me they were so overbooked that I'd need to call back in a week. And so the process of learning the anatomy of my fear began.

I knew it was important that I go within my mind to sort things out—both regarding the professor and my own ideas about fear, sexual shame, punishment and guilt, and death. Remember, dearies, that the wages of sin is death and that has been drummed into us over the years. And sex outside of marriage was taught to me as certainly sinful; hence, I will die because of it. I was amazed at how all these old messages were worming their way into my normally joyful attitude. They were so irrational I couldn't believe I still harbored them somewhere so deep in my psyche. People started asking me what was wrong, which made me feel even more afraid and ashamed. I tried nurturing myself with bubble baths and candlelight, which normally make me feel beautiful, blessed, and also sexual. However, every time I would think or feel sexual, I felt panic. It was a very unhealthy mental state. I continued to tell myself positive things and work through my terror. I went into childhood issues of being beaten and told I was abnormal because of alleged masturbation. I remembered my mother threatening she would drag me to the doctor to show him what a pervert she had for a child. Then, among my psychological garbage, I remembered almost dying twice from tubular pregnancies, again sex and death related. I went back in time and mind to when my husband told the world I was a slut because I wouldn't be celibate for him. He considered celibacy to be fidelity because when I was thirty he became ill and no longer wanted sex in any form. When I finally told him I wouldn't sneak around and I could not live without sex the rest of my life, he insisted on divorce. Yet he told everyone, including me, that I was an unfit mother because of my sexual attitudes and needs. All of the pain around these emotionally charged issues came back, including all of my anger. It was 'in my face'. I *had* to work through it to get to the other side. But what surprised me most of all is how difficult it was to dispel my fear due to ancient resentments and deeply engraved guilt and shame.

I was angry, and my fear was merely a cover-up emotion. These ancient memories were trying their best to do me in, quite literally.

In a week I called back. The date I called back happened to be a significantly lucky number in my life. The appointment was for the following week. However, my code had two more significant numbers in my life—a talisman to get me through the dangerous forest unscathed. That was a little consolation. I went about my life, but it was not easy. I tried to be unafraid, but couldn't pull it off. I was afraid.

When the time came, I got on a bus to the clinic. I felt like throwing up, but looked out the window and tried to amuse myself by looking at the passing pedestrians. I soothed myself with prayer. I got to the clinic and they were showing AIDS videos. Again I tried to keep my equilibrium. After my counseling session they drew blood. Each person who dealt with me was gentle and reassuring. Now I had to wait another three weeks for the results to come in.

Three weeks is a long time when viewed in this context. Yet I hoped the result of my soul searching would bring me out of the woods emotionally. Negative scenarios would start to play in my head and I would have to dispel Demon Fear with nurturing and loving messages. I told several friends, both male and female, because I realized one of the big issues was shame. The only thing that takes power out of shame is a bright light called open, honest sharing. If I didn't, I was judging myself as bad because of something that is too shameful to share.

The three weeks felt like years. I could not work on my book, especially since it was about sex. Television seemed inane. I could go to the gym. I could be with friends. I could read. But in the middle of the night sometimes I would awaken, and again Demon Fear would start the mental movies of shame and death.

Finally the day came. I got dressed up beautifully, put on a fashionable hat, and got on the bus. I was no longer afraid. I felt as though I was going to be liberated. One hour left. However, when I was called and a new counselor directed me down a long, narrow hallway, silently, my heart stopped. She knew the results that were in my closed file folder and she seemed somber. Now I started to sweat. My heart felt like a brick. At the end of the hallway she turned, and there was another waiting room. Why? Why did she take me so far back? Then she turned into her office and slowly closed the door. Still seemingly somber, she asked me to sit down. She started, "Now before we go any further, I need to ask you some questions...." I was horrified, and painfully pleaded, "Please, by the way you're acting, you're scaring me to death. Am I all right or not?" I wanted to cry as though it were spanning my moment of birth to my moment of death. Her face softened with a deep smile and she thanked me for being so honest with her. She then opened the file and responded, "We ask you questions about your zip code and age so we can compare to make sure it is your result and not someone else's. See, this is your number, and you see here it says 'non-reactive', which means you are okay. But I want you to look at the form so you can see for yourself." My tears combined with my clouded lenses, and I couldn't read it. But I squinted to see the verdict of my pain, and when I did, I started to cry with relief. She held me in her arms, and I told her I was so grateful to have gone through the experience of waiting. I shared with her how much I had learned about fear in those three weeks, how I had cleared up some old destructive sexual issues, and how I would be able to help others because of knowing such intense debilitating pain and fear, and just how to work through those issues to dispel the negativity.

And I did learn. I learned to use condoms. I learned what self-honesty really means and I learned courage. And I learned truly that fear is far more damaging than any other human emotion. My compassion has increased for those who are told the opposite answer and have their worst fear realized. There is no judgment. Pain and fear are demonic teachers to help us learn to live and be compassionate for others and for ourselves.

I occasionally heard from Herr Professor afterwards. I always politely refused his dates, and I'm still not angry. I learned a valuable lesson about myself. And besides that, he taught me to use a condom in the condo.

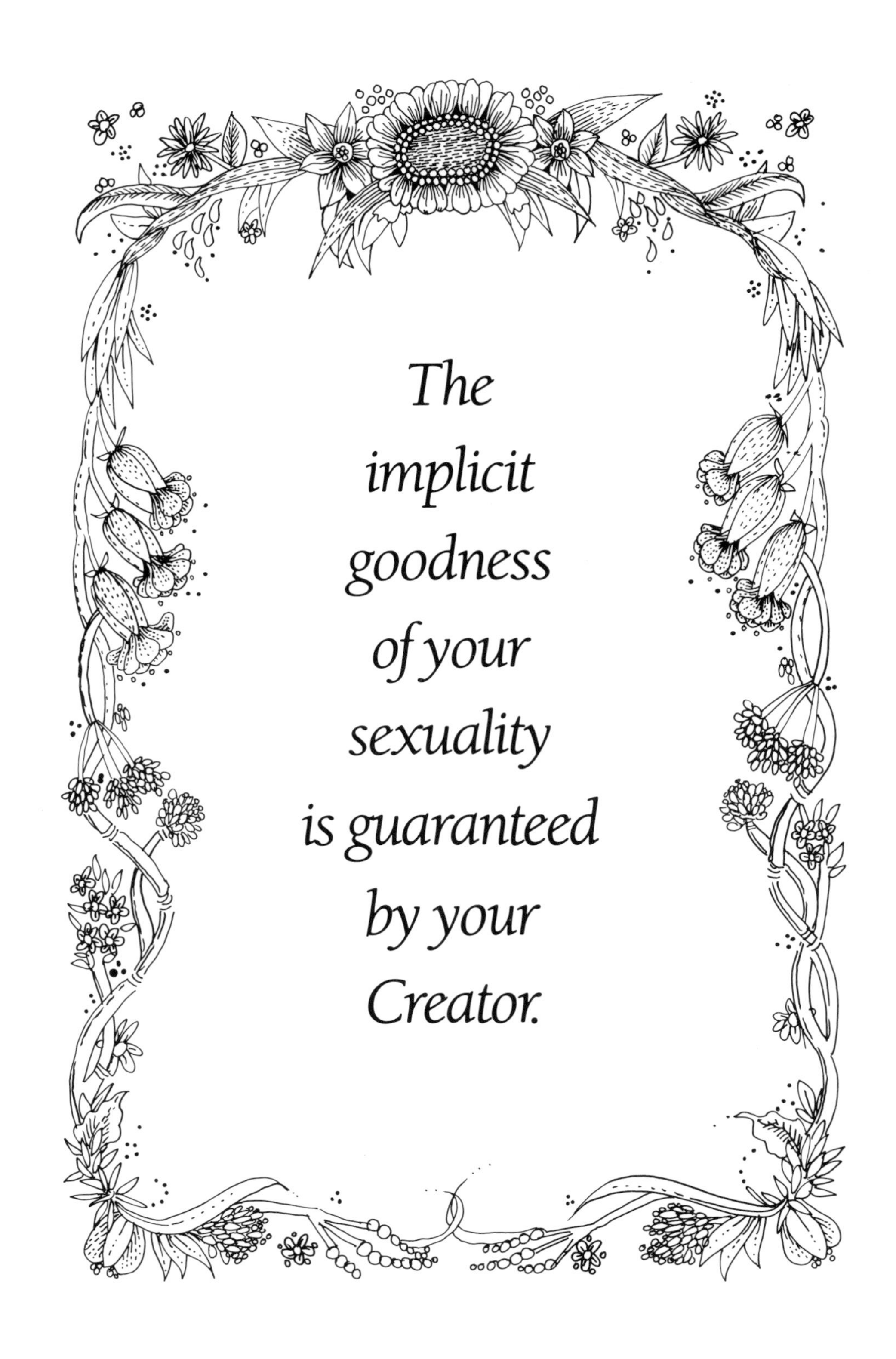

The
implicit
goodness
of your
sexuality
is guaranteed
by your
Creator.

Sex as Your Own Garden

Advertising has all but ruined our opinions of our physical bodies. Open any magazine, especially a fashion magazine. Most people's sex lives are quite inhibited because of the self-conscious comparisons we make to fantasy fashion models. The reason I say 'fantasy' is because the photos are retouched by computer, so much so that they could be called revised rather than retouched. Our models don't look nearly that good in person either, so don't judge yourself by the impossible ideal. We are especially vulnerable whenever someone sees us naked. Even the word 'naked' smacks of ugliness. 'Disrobe'. 'Undress'. None of these words have poetry in their sounds. And making love is a living act of poetry. It is a poem that starts in our soul like a quivering bird needing to fly and to soar to freedom.

You may wish to tape record this chapter after reading it so you can have it in your own voice to use in the future. Change the words in any way that you choose. It is your tape and your journey.

We're going to go on a voyage of the mind. It might be good to put on some soothing music. If you're not alone now, find a secluded place where you won't be disturbed – a comfortable room or a nice setting outdoors if the weather and total privacy permit. Put on some loose, comfortable clothing – a soft robe would be best. It is time to relax and be alone with yourself for a while. Set aside at least a half hour.

Now, sit back, relax, and erase your thoughts, whatever they are. Imagine taking a damp cloth, and in your mind, slowly wipe the blackboard clean. Or, picture the keys on the keyboard of your computer that delete and erase the disk of your mind, because this time is for you, only you. That special you that has feelings and desires. The you that is no other, who wants to touch the world with your specialness.

If the computer image doesn't work for you, imagine placing your cares in a beautifully carved box that has a very heavy lid. They'll be quite protected and they'll wait. Let your spirit be free for a while. You deserve it. You're going to be free now, unjudged and unjudging, free and uninhibited, poetic and passionate, vibrant and alive with wishes and images of fantasy, imagining the finest feast possible. A feast fit for royalty, for you are royal. A feast of many courses, cooked and prepared for you especially, with exotic spices, subtle and wild, from an untamed garden.

See yourself in a filmy gown or a soft loin cloth. Your feet are bare. You look at the ground under you, and a gentle breeze blows your garment softly. Look down now. The grass is rich beneath your feet. Soft, luxurious. Alive and tingling. Close your eyes for a moment, appreciating this wonderful warmth and freedom you experience. And then, slowly step down the path. Breathe the air deeply and taste the fragrances with your inward breath, your mouth slightly open. Breathe through your mouth and feel the cooling air on your tongue, down your throat. Feel your throat muscles loosen, your jaw muscles melt. Your cells shiver with delight. Surely the specialness of this day is an omen. It is perfect in every way, and you get an insight that shows you your own perfection, just as you are.

Now, continue down the path. Notice the beautiful trees on every side of you which seem to spread open as you pass, making your way gentle and easy. Look beneath you. Your bare feet feel the coolness of the soft, loamy path, moist but not wet, which winds downward into a cool ravine, and you hear the gentle splashing of a stream. The water sounds sensual and your groin slowly becomes engorged with warm blood. Your breathing becomes deeper and rhythmic with your steps, and the musical sound of the water takes its song into your veins. Each heartbeat is felt as sexual pleasure as it passes your groin. Your body is living and breathing sound. Vibration. A resonating and pulsing energy that on another level of hearing would sound like music. For it is true. Your sexuality brings music and life to your body. Your beautifully expressive body. Your tender and loving, sexually alive body.

Your thoughts clear once more, and the sound of a bird and then many birds fills your senses. It is sunset. The shadows add their artistic touch to the forest, which is thinning now. You walk into a luxurious grassy clearing and you notice a smooth, flat boulder almost directly in the center. As you approach, you feel as though you have been here before. In a dream. In another time. Actually you have been here many times, but like *deja vu,* you can't quite put your finger on when. You lie down on the rock's smooth surface and feel the warmth of the absorbed sunlight under your body. You quiver with surging feelings of pleasure. The sun is behind the trees by now, but you still can feel its warm and penetrating rays coming through the shimmering leaves to your heart, your stomach, your forehead, the soles of your feet. And you feel the rock's vibrations coming strongly now into your sexual areas, which are awake, perhaps needing fulfillment of your sensual, and possibly erotic wishes. Or, if not erotic, at least enjoying the fullness and richness of your physical body in a more passive way. Whichever you choose, that is what is right for you.

Sex is a gift of the Universe. Energy pulsing from the center expanding outward in warm waves and eventually in wild and pounding waves. Waves that make both loud and softly soothing noises as they hit the shore. Waves that totally give themselves without judging the sand. Continual waves. Splashing again, again, again. Expressing their life. Giving vibrancy to the sand on which they land. In joy just to be, to give, and to trust and abandon themselves without fighting it, without a program, and only expression of life as their goal.

This is your sexuality. What your sexuality is when you let it be, and let it become. This is a journey you can take anytime you wish. Open your robe now so you can feel your skin. Use your hands to feel your body. Feel *your* special touch on *your* skin. What it feels like to your hand, your fingers, your palm. What it feels like to the sensitive skin on the front of your torso. How your body longs to be touched. Don't stop. Don't inhibit yourself. Allow yourself to be and to feel. It is your birthright. And you are good. It is the murmer and pulsing life of the cells in your body. It is life. It is living art. Continue your fantasy on the rock in the clearing and when you are finished, we'll talk some more. Be sexual if you desire. If you do not desire to be sexual right now, be sensual. Give the special touch of love and acceptance to your body. You deserve to be loved and taken care of, and paid attention to. Even by you.

While your feelings are still fresh, let's talk about what happened to you. Could you relax enough to enjoy yourself? Did you really enjoy yourself, or just sort of? Because whatever your feelings were, those are likely the feelings you now demonstrate with your sex partner. And, they are truly vibrations of energy. You tune your emotions to subtle frequencies of communication. If you choose not to tune them, you literally are 'turned off' and, sad to say, a turn-off as well. And as the night follows the day, so too will your partner be or become turned off. We have to be tuned in to ourselves and the other to make sex a communication of body, mind, and spirit. As even the bits in computer chips are charged or not charged, there is no middle ground.

If you were turned off or felt guilty in this subtle exercise of touching your body, it is going to be very difficult for you to accept any coaching on giving good oral sex, which we are going to get into shortly. You will necessarily phase out with some excuse so you don't have to deal with your feelings.

I personally think it is exciting to know that we are animals. Wow! Not only purring and breathing hard, but really roaring, hissing, growling, and screaming animals! But just try to let it out. "Oh, my God! The neighbors will think you're killing me and call the police, or worse, they'll actually realize we're having sex!" "The children will hear us." Or, "It's bad enough that my makeup is all smeared. I'll be darned if I'm going to let myself grunt as though I'm having a difficult bowel movement." "Eyes rolled back in my head? Are you nuts?" "You want me to open my mouth and just let it hang open like a psychotic?" In a way, really good sex is literally close to going out of your mind. You *are* losing control, at least of your logical left brain. It is definitely an altered state of consciousness, and to a rational human that is scary stuff. So, if you can't let go all at once, do it one step at a time, until you're quite comfortable. But at least try to let go a little more each time. Most of all, don't judge yourself—with your breathing, allow yourself to go deeper into the ecstatic reverie. Choose it. Follow it. Become the moment rather than watching it.

Freedom: to be free, to move your body freely as your emotions flow or explode. Freedom from fear, and freedom from being judged. When you can't or rather won't let yourself experience your own erotic sounds when you have sex, it really boils down to your clinging desperately to a static self-image that can't crack enough to be real. The carrot to change is that the more sound you make and the more naturally you can emote, the stronger your orgasm will be, the more sincere and wild and passionate you will be, and the more power of life you will exude to your partner. All those sounds you're so afraid to make will actually turn your lover on, not off, and will make him or her wild and strong and vibrant as well. The sounds of sex will excite you and stimulate you both to the very peaks of thrilling human passion. Silent orgasms can be intense, too, but once you allow yourself the permission to make sounds, I believe you will stay in that mode—stereo over mono any day!

Now, let's go back to the lovely and sweet or wild and passionate fantasy you just had. I wager you came close to an orgasmic climax, and perhaps fell or leaped right over the highest cliff of ecstasy quite weightlessly, or barbarically and wildly ejaculated into the air. It was a very erotic scene that was set—the sun, the rock, the hand on your warm skin. All erotic thoughts should turn you on. Anything sensual will arouse you if you don't repress yourself, and if you don't judge yourself. When you are worried about looking or sounding stupid when you are having sex, you are judging yourself. You are editing your human nature.

I am going to ask you to go through this day—the whole day—being turned on by sounds, smells, by beautiful scenes or people, by the moon, by your awareness of your sexual juices, by the turn of a leg or shoulder, or someone's full mouth. By your thoughts, provocative advertisements. By clothing or the lack thereof. Just be tuned in to the body channel rather than the mind channel. Observe yourself today. Be aware of your feelings of sexuality today. Try to stay actively aware of your body when your mind doesn't need to function—at lunch, or in the moments between the moments when you have to concentrate. Create your own short fantasy that you can meander back to from time to time. We'll talk this evening and compare notes. Terrific! Meet you later and, yes, have a very sensual day.

Flirting

Most Americans have a very rigid attitute about what flirting means. Any person who has observed the French or Germanic culture will see everybody flirting all the time. It does not mean you are going to jump into the sack with everyone you flirt with. Flirting is an attitude of sensuality, a reminder of our sensual nature, and an impetus to remind even the married that they are sexually desirable. The only time flirting is totally out of line is when you are with your significant other, or the other person is. Then it is not only rude but damaging. It is at that moment an act of emotional violence.

Sometimes flirting does not even have sexual connotations. I flirt with children constantly. Peek-a-boo is flirting. It is eye contact that brings you into the game of being human. I once was standing in a bank line in Mexico. The bank was horrendously crowded, and there was a 3-year-old boy who was totally bored and trying to amuse himself without getting into trouble. It was very, very hot. I felt his dilemma in my heart because I knew he would eventually get hollered at. I was holding my sun hat in my hands, and all at once I had the irresistible urge to play peek-a-boo with him. He caught the invitation immediately (and it was done with a very subtle gesture). It not only kept him out of displeasure for fifteen minutes, it changed the energy in the entire room. I was the only American, and despite the lack of cultural and economic sameness, the love that was displayed in our playfulness turned an impatient, hot, uncomfortable crowd into their childlike hearts. The wait seemed shorter, happiness overcame discomfort, and the boy and I amused both his parents and the bank customers as well as ourselves. Children are not bad, they are bored, and flirting with them brings me a childlike happiness. It is certainly not sexual. So this is the best example of flirting I can show to make it less threatening.

The problem most people have with flirting is the fear of making and keeping eye contact. Many people have a hard enough time making eye contact. Sustaining it can be psychologically intolerable to most people. It makes them uncomfortable and embarrassed. If the person is sexually appealing to you, it seems to be even more difficult. A psych teacher once told my class, "Embarrassment is secret joy." When you make eye contact with a person, there is a little chill that goes through the body—the skin's responding to the moment. I would call that secret joy. But there is another problem we have that is deeper, and that is the fear to get close. Behind that fear lies another—the fear to be known. We often go through an entire life afraid to know ourselves or let others close enough to truly know us. Eye contact will open the door to knowing yourself. It's like peeking into a forbidden room, and the room is you. So if that intrigues you, try it. In little doses at first, getting used to it, with "Good morning," which is even less threatening than "Hi." The more you practice, the easier it becomes. Then you can add a smile, or forget the 'good morning' and just smile. You will get discriminating and know who is open and who is not open, so rejection will become less. You will also gain a sixth sense about when it is safe and when it may be dangerous. Children naturally have that ability if they're not interferred with, and we do, too, when we trust ourselves. When I get rejection from a smile or a greeting (women and men, for this is a social, not a sexual exercise) I tell myself, "That's okay, it's his problem, not mine, and I have more smiles left." Or, "She's not quite there yet. That's okay." This reminder takes away the feeling that my smile was spurned or my good will trampled as they walked by, or I somehow lost it or wasted it. This seems to keep me from becoming angry and closing off. They might not even be rejecting my smile, but somewhere off in their own little world or surprised and confused by the gesture. Occasional rejection becomes acceptable and even necessary because it makes me stronger. By remaining open, and continuing to greet people, I can take people's rejection without its damaging my psyche. You see, a psyche needs to get exercise, to be flexible and strong, just like a muscle. There is always rejection somewhere out there. It is not everywhere, only somewhere. And it does not always reflect on your ability to communicate, but possibly on theirs. Remember that, especially when you practice. But do practice, or your psyche muscle will never get strong enough to be able to flirt wisely and happily. And, it's a good way to make friends. The way to avoid feeling like you have an ulterior motive is not to have one. Accepting rejection well even when you're turned on to someone eliminates the guilty feeling of having an ulterior motive. I notice when I'm in a great mood, everyone responds well. When I'm in an average mood, I get about 50%, and when I'm in a so-so mood, I get a so-so response. It may be that I get exactly what I give.

After you become comfortable with flirting without a sexual connotation, you are ready to practice flirting as a sexual communication. This may or may not be with the implication of further permission or hopes. Remember this. You can subtly imply a desire to see the person again, or you can be direct and simply say, "I like you. I'd like to see you again." However, if you've made no direct implication, and one has been inferred, and a misunderstanding takes place that there should be further contact and you were being misleading or teasing, don't be bullied. You are not responsible for the other person misunderstanding and taking your flirting as an invitation to your bedroom. Guilt is a powerful line. Don't buy it. However, make sure your rejection is kindly and lightly delivered in the same playful way, unless the person is rude, in which case say, "Excuse me", and walk away. Any polite offer is a gift of compliment, and should be accepted or refused as a polite gift.

Some people can be friendly to everyone *except* those to whom they are attracted. This is a tragedy, but can be remedied with practice. I was there once, and the way I grew through the situation was to admit to myself that my sexuality was human and not to be ashamed of. Once I could own that acceptance, it was easier for me to speak to those who attracted me – not just those who didn't. If they were not attracted to me, it was obvious immediately, but if they were, the risk was worth taking. You must remember that rejection does not mean you are no good. It simply means 'no thank you'. Attraction is not always mutual, and if it is mutual, it is not always possible. It does not mean unworthiness. It just means 'no thank you'. It will toughen your skin a little. No one likes to be around a thin-skinned person anyway (one who gets hurt easily and has no rebounding power). So take it in stride, keep your sense of humor and perspective, and keep moving.

Eye contact will become easier and even more desirable, and it is very rewarding. It will start you on the road to total self-acceptance, because you will realize we are all alike in many ways. We all want and need to be recognized, cherished and loved for who we are. We all need to be respected and responded to. And to get these things we have to give these things. Eye contact will get you closer to yourself as well as to the other. It will make you more compassionate. You will end up being sensitive enough to see people's sadness, joy and fear. And you then will be able to see when *you* are admired and appreciated as well. Self-centered fear of embarrassment keeps you looking for rejection. Think about others rather than yourself, and you will lose your fear. Eye contact is an adventure. Stay in the moment. Do not assume what another person thinks or feels. Go with the excitement of *not* knowing, like children do. Be curious. Look at faces non-judgmentally. It will be apparent you are not judging, and it will bring you close to people because they will intuitively trust you. People know when you are judging them and when you are not judging them. You will become more alive, more fun to be with. And it will be a door to a magnificent palace of many rooms with more doors to open. Don't be afraid to smile. Look deeply into people's eyes. Be there. They will be there back, looking at you too, so don't worry about your stupid makeup or hairdo or shoes or shirt. By all means be friendly, not intense. Just be free and friendly and fun and present.

What you will notice immediately is that flirting makes you feel more alive, sexually and in general. The fact of your maleness or femaleness will resonate in your inner core, in your outer molecules, and within and beyond your physical boundary. It will also make the other person feel that aliveness. I believe this feeling is one of the ways your body uses to stay healthy. It is a wonderful way to stay healthy and aware. It not only feels good, it will, in fact, enliven you to a fuller capacity. Acknowledging and integrating your sexuality into your total personhood rather than obliterating it or relegating it to a obscure corner of your life will enhance your life—not just your body, but your spirit and total lifeforce. Be alive in your sexuality always. Of course, I don't mean horny and obscene. Be sensually alive not just when you're getting ready for the culmination of the feeling. Acknowledge your sexuality when you look into a mirror. Thank the Universe for it. Honor it with your love and accept it with full embodiment and response-ability. You exist in a wonderful and sexual body. That is truly a gift of Nature, and of your own personal Creator.

Some days you won't feel like being that friendly because you'll be in a quieter mood. But by and large, remember to practice being friendly. Challenge yourself daily to say 'good morning' to at least ten people you don't know until it becomes a habit and you're totally comfortable with it. You'll get better with time at picking the ones who give back and avoiding the ones whose eyes clearly say 'keep off the grass,' (although some of them may fool you and only appear to be stern). It once took me two years of saying 'hello' to a certain person before he started to respond. It was good practice for my patience and non-judgmental attitude. And since we all need a 'hello', give the curmudgeons a shot too. It will show you how wrong negative judgment can be. If you are confident of yourself when you greet people, they will be more apt to respond positively. A tentative greeting because of lack of self-assuredness may get a tentative or negative response, so remember their response can be your mirror. If you don't believe you're worthy of a kind reply, you probably won't get one.

Make this a part of your daily routine. You will meet many wonderful people. Because, secretly or obviously, all of us are wonderful people. Dare to look. Dare to feel. Dare to take the risk of being human.

Erotic Kissing

I stood six inches from his face. I could feel the air between our faces alive with an energy impossible to describe. This is the only man in my life who knows what a kiss is: what the air between the faces can do; how to transfer his whole energy pattern into mine without devouring my special space; how to enter that space and merge with it, tickling every molecule of air and flesh until there is no difference.

I keep wondering why so few men know how to do this magical act. In trying to analyze it, at least the reason why they never learn, is that they don't bother. Kissing doesn't seem to be important to most men because it is too preliminary to the goal-orientation of sexual intercourse. The lack of proficiency comes strictly from goal orientation – impatience for immediate gratification. I think their lack of interest also is because kissing is relegated to the category of 'foreplay'. We know our whole culture suffers from the desire for immediate gratification: fast foods; media; facsimile; and computers. Even reading a book is a bothersome chore to many in this alleged Age of Information. Just give me the facts, Ma'am. So, too, with kissing and other light, erotic niceties. For most men, their goal is the orgasm rather than the journey into it, with it, and out of it. Kissing is just a way of making a woman hot enough to say 'yes' and wet enough to enter, not something to enjoy in itself. That sounds crass, but it's true. Kissing as a way of communicating one's soul to its very depths has been lost, tossed and forgotten as an art. The tickle of air between the faces before they touch, the dizziness and loss of boundary, the curiosity and somewhat awkward feeling of discovery, and the thrill are abandoned for more expedient measures. Sports are goal-oriented, business is goal-oriented, and different lifestyles have produced a culture of men and women who can barely communicate.

I can't imagine why anyone would want to bypass and even avoid this delicious act. And I am sure there are others who can't imagine wasting their time with such foolish pastimes.

It seems as though most women are process-oriented, and most men are goal-oriented. Goal orientation makes erotic kissing merely a preliminary, which can even perhaps be bypassed if the man knows the woman will acquiesce anyway.

When the man I mentioned comes near me, I start to tremble emotionally and physically. Sometimes when he touches me I actually vibrate. I am so in the moment I can't even think of what will happen next. I am so there, in that incredible spell of wonder, that everything else dissolves. If I had the choice of kissing him and not having intercourse, or having intercourse and not kissing him, I would definitely choose the kissing. I don't think I'm an unusual woman, so this probably is true for most women. Women love to be kissed—unless sex is a perfunctory duty to an undesired mate. Unfortunately, I have been in this situation also.

So it seems that women might enjoy kissing more than men. Since women take longer for arousal than men, it is important for men to use this wonderful way to discover their potency. When a man feels the woman respond so completely to his presence, it must make his own sense of sexual reality even stronger. He becomes a truly potent and valid presence.

I read an interview in which Barbara De Angelis, author of *How to Make Love All the Time,* encourages the concept of the 20-second kiss. She recommends it three times a day. That way, when lovemaking to its full erotic completion is appropriate, the connection will be more of a continuum rather than an abrupt occurrence. I cheer her thoughts.

Knowing how to kiss, however, is *not* how to kiss. 'Do this, do that' won't work. Each kiss is a happening, with its own rhythm and style. Spontaneity is the secret, and innocent discovery is the path. Not knowing how to approach, being slightly tentative and shy, feeling awkward, not knowing when exactly, or how exactly, to approach is all important to feel and enjoy the experience. The kiss will evolve as it progresses. It will just happen. Even with couples who have been together for a long time, each kiss can still be a new delight.

You might feel awkward and even confused at times when you kiss, perhaps even dizzy. But confusion is charming. Enjoy it. Make it part of your journey to discover yourself as well as the other.

I really don't like it if a man kisses me too suddenly or puts his tongue in my mouth in the manner of an invader rather than a discoverer. I want him to discover me. I need him to be curious and excited. I want to enjoy the subtle fragrance of his skin. I need to enjoy the approach and the wonder. I do not want him to spear my epiglottis. A strong man is a gentle man, not a sexual Genghis Khan. A man does not need to use power to be powerful. It reminds me of the song lyric about needing a lover with a slow hand and an easy touch. That song wasn't a hit for nothing. If a woman backs up when a man kisses her, he is probably too strong, too fast, too deep.

People should kiss a lot. As a society we are finally learning to hug each other, so maybe it's time we learn to kiss each other more often and more sensually. The fact that each kiss is truly unique should elate you. Nothing is ever the same unless you make it the same. And the word 'make' involves a predisposition to form. Kissing at its best should be formless. Just let it happen naturally, but let it happen more often. If you are a woman, develop your sense of inviting the kiss, making yourself more open to approach. In other words, become approachable. And if you are a man, approach the other with gentle restraint and desire. Also, reversal of traditional roles is often desirable, where the woman can easily approach the man with gentle restraint. Gentle restraint is not sexual hesitation. There is a difference. One is confident, the other is fearful. You will become powerful at sharing. It is an inner power that comes with the peace of just being yourself and accepting yourself for who you are. Kissing is a wonderful way of sharing who you are.

Remember when you were young and you used to neck? I think if we return to necking more often we will reclaim our youthful desire. Even goal-oriented people will benefit because they will likely reach their goal a lot more often if they reclaim the romantic, youthful joy of the kiss.

Using Your Hands and Skin

The most magical sex organ of all is the skin. And the skin loves to be touched, caressed, fondled, tickled, licked, scratched. It likes air, water, heat, cool, to be covered, to be bared, to be breathed on and nibbled. Throughout the entire act of sex the skin should be continually tantalized. It's the skin of your arm reaching out to touch, not the bone. It's the skin on your face or behind your ear that needs to be touched with the tongue. And it's the skin on your tongue that wants the experience, not the muscle. And, most of all, it's the skin on your penis that wants to be licked and caressed, or the skin on your labia and on your clit, if you are female, that needs stimulation. Skin is the singlemost erotic organ of your body. And it is the singlemost erotic organ on your partner's body. Use that awareness. Think of all the possible erotic things you can do to someone else's skin. Experiment and see what you can do to stimulate each other's skin without actually having intercourse. It probably won't be too long before you get so crazy with passion that you devour each other in an incredible, final, erotic act of sex.

Yet, how many people don't use their fingertips to tickle or use their nails to arouse. How many people take the skin for granted, other than the skin on their genitals. Such a waste of creativity. Skin exudes your very essense, the scent that is purely you. No one else's scent is the same, and when you really get into it, you know that full well.

The other day I ran into a friend on the 'L' platform. He and I don't have anything sexual going. We sometimes eat at the same restaurant at lunchtime and are laughing friends. We appreciate each other and love each other as lighthearted buddies. He had a book and said strongly as we got onto the train, "I'll sit next to you and protect you (there had been some trouble recently), but I want to read." Understanding totally and not at all feeling rejected, I humorously reassured him telling him I would probably feel his leg, but I promised I wouldn't talk. Of course he knew I was joking, but after he got settled and was reading his book, he took my hand quite comfortably. Throughout the whole ride he gently caressed it, tickled it, slid his finger suggestively in and out of little crevices, and was generally exceedingly erotic in his suggestive symbolic gestures. It is certainly an art, holding a hand well and turning someone on by such a subtle touch that no one else on the train knew what was happening. And he did it just because it was fun, and he knew he could, and he knew I would understand and not make a big deal out of it.

It made me think again of why it is so thrilling to have my lover put his finger(s) in my mouth, or why, now that I have overcome my shyness, when I am very erotically enjoying a kiss, I like to put my finger in his mouth or in between our mouths so I can feel both my finger and our tongues at the same time, or why I like to put my fingers on my genitals so I can feel his tongue there at the same time. It is wonderfully erotic because of the symbolism. There is no other way I can show my male desire to enjoy entering any other way. And maybe that's why slipping the end of a wet finger gently into his anal opening while I have his gorgeous cock in my mouth is such a thrill for me, and obviously for him. It's a healthy way of playing the opposite role. Remember, of course, not to put your finger in his or your mouth later unless you can get to a sink first (which is imperative at an appropriate pause in the romancing).

All of this may be quite familiar to you or quite new. I had to discover such erotic delights all on my own, so maybe you can enjoy them a few years sooner than I did. I just became curious enough and bold enough to experiment with what I wanted to do without judging myself.

Especially when you can shower just before you enter the bedroom, and you have washed each other's hair and skin rather than your own. Then you can even lick and suck each other's toes without fear of offense. I suggest only one person being active at a time, because it is an incredible thrill just passively to lie there while someone is taking their pleasure just licking you to drive you wild. There's enough time for both of you, but one at a time is intensely more erotic, and the build-up is phenomenal. Now is the time to practice making noises if you are shy. Breathing in through your teeth, out with a sigh or cry. Let yourself experiment with your own sounds.

After taking inventory, we have ten fingers, ten nails, two hands, arms, breasts with nipples, ears, a tongue, throat, lots of juices, eyes which can take in or express, breath, one highly appropriately divided derrière, genitals, legs and feet with ten toes. All of these can be expressive sexual organs during the sex act. Every one of them has movement capabilities in any possible combination and sequence—a veritable symphony of erotic organs. Oh, yes, I forgot: vocal chords to say w-o-r-d-s as well as sexual noises.

"Oh, my God, now she's going to tell me to talk dirty." That's right, I am. You know why? I'll tell you a little story.

I wanted to say certain things that I felt, using *those words*. The ones I couldn't say. I knew he would never turn on to, "I'd like to put my mouth on your penis." No, 'penis' just didn't make it in the turn-on category. You mean ME say COCK or SUCK? Yes. That's exactly what I mean. If you're scandalized by that, you need to take inventory of whose sexual attitudes you have or are reflecting: your own or those of your parent/religion/society. I had to write the things down that I wanted to say and then recite what I wrote over and over. At first it was embarrassing to say it aloud even to myself in private. I got better, though. It got easier. It took time. Then I actually tried it, and I was scared, first on the phone (it was easier) and then finally in bed. Now I can't believe there was a time when I couldn't talk erotically. I talk erotically to myself, too, sometimes, when I just want to turn myself on. It feels good. Maybe I'm unusual. In any case, that's how this one woman learned to say erotic things comfortably. I practiced, and I encourage you to do the same. If any little teeny weeny part of your psyche responds with disgust to this, you'd better be honest, because healthy sexual acceptance of yourself is the key to healing many self-esteem problems–problems that cannot exist in an open mind. Verbal expression is not twisted or perverse.

Words are an aphrodisiac. All sound can be an aphrodisiac. Don't leave them out because you think you'll sound vulgar. Sexy sounds and words are not vulgar, they're dirty. A long time ago a famous comedian was asked if he thought sex was dirty. He replied, "Of course it is. If it's done right."

Use words as an aphrodisiac. It's really fun to get so relaxed and non-judgmental that if you think something, you can say it without fear.

Dare to experiment! Give yourself and your partner the pleasure of turning on to your own words and fantasies.

Touching and Hugging

Throughout the centuries European people have expressed themselves using their hands. The more expressively and passionately people talk, the more they use their hands. The more affectionate people are, the more they touch you. Touching you with honor is one of the finest compliments a person can give you. I'm not talking about invasive pawing or mauling, and I'm not talking about catch-my-drift poking.

Hands express love, passion, or inhibition. They are extensions of our minds at work expressing happiness or sadness, trust or fear, passion or self-doubt. How you use your hands during sex will be a barometer of how you feel about yourself.

Also, how you feel about your hands is important in using them creatively during sex. If you have a problem with loving your hands, or thinking about their lack of beauty, figure out why. You should smooth out the rough edges so you don't scratch or injure your lover. Remember, your hands give you beautiful service throughout your entire life, and to ignore them is unkind. Unconditional use and acceptance of your hands are very important because your lover needs to be touched with utmost care and communication, especially during sex. If you don't touch him or her with that care, it may be taken as rejection, and he or she will feel untouchable or undesirable in some way. A woman will likely think her body isn't beautiful, especially given the ridiculously altered photographs that appear in all the men's magazines as the ideal body. A man may interpret lack of touch as coldness in a woman, or infer that she doesn't really want him. Most people think their bodies are not beautiful. This is sad, but true. Notice how many people cannot take a compliment about themselves. They either push it away or come back with self-deprecation. Much of this is because we are not touched enough in a positive, affirming way, either verbally or physically.

Hugging is one of the universal and least threatening types of touch that is the most satisfying. Shaking hands is rather cold, but can be warm if the communication is not stilted. Hugging as a greeting, if it is not business, can be acceptable if done in a non-sexual way. It will take practice and it will feel awkward at first, but when it comes from the heart, it is usually accepted as it's meant.

There are hugs, and there are *hugs*. The longer hug is an embrace and, again, is not necessarily sexual. It can be between parent and child, friends, lovers as friends, and can be extended to any person in non-violent emotional distress. Of course, discretion should always be used. This type of hug is much more satisfying, but also much more difficult to give or receive because it involves emotional intimacy. There is a dissolving of boundaries in an embrace—a place where 'you' and 'I' become 'we'. Everyone needs this deep form of emotional physical contact. It sometimes involves an initial feeling of discomfort that says, "This is long enough." This point is usually not long enough to satisfy a person's longing to be held. When you feel that nagging urge to pull away, the other person feels your withdrawal. Their temptation is to interpret your withdrawal as rejection. If you can resist your discomfort at this point, and just stay a little longer, you will increase your ability to be emotionally intimate. Realize it is a fear of intimacy—sometimes felt even as the threat of being 'swallowed up' by the other, or the fear of commitment because of intimacy. Overcome the fear. Pulling away too soon is one of the biggest hurdles to overcome before you can truly embrace another. Stay longer, and when you start to feel uncomfortable, realize it is your own fear that is working on you. That fear is usually based on *perceived* rejection and fear of abandonment. "I'll leave you before you can leave me." It comes from unresolved childhood issues that will play themselves out again and again in your life until you work through them. In the case of the hugger—the person who initiated the hug—it is fear of being inappropriate. In the case of the huggee, it is fear of not being adequate. Both feelings are possible. In either case, overcome it. Stay in the embrace longer or ask the other person to keep holding you. It will be worth all the diamonds and gold in the world. Being held with love is the backbone of all emotional security. Nobody gets enough, so do it often, many people, both sexes, sincerely, awkwardly, smoothly, any way—but do it. Also, try not to stick out your derrière so only your shoulders get touched. Stand straight, tall, and be there.

Touching, hugging and embracing are especially wonderful when they include your sexuality. Now you can be entirely uninhibited because the message is clear—sexual contact is desired. We have limited ways in which we have allowed ourselves to express touch. We usually never question this or bother to explore touching further than ordinary unimaginative contact. There are many creative ways of touching another, with all aspects of one's body on all aspects of theirs, with different pressure, different rhythm, and even with different objects which can create exotic pleasure—not just artificial sex toys, but feathers, clothing, jewelry, and other natural objects. Think of touching as music. You would much rather listen to music that has tonal quality, dynamics, rhythm and variety. Monotone is just that—monotonous. Musical touch is similar in its need to express. Touching can be teasing. It can be the final fulfillment. It should be the unraveling of tantalizing pleasure.

Touching another's face is a very sensual act—caressing the hair, skin, and feeling the ears and the back of the neck—especially with the tongue. As I have said, one of the most sensual feelings I've ever felt is putting my hand up during kissing and feeling the lips and the inside of our mouths and where they come together, feeling both my tongue and his with my finger. It was very scary to attempt the first time. I felt I was being inappropriately curious. But I suspended judgment of myself and did it anyway. This is very important during creative sex—you have no measurement of what is appropriate. You must suspend judgment of yourself (the you that is watching you), and actually dismiss this intruding third party altogether. The natural you will be totally appropriate and balanced, and totally there. Someone once said, "It's always best to be yourself, because no one knows if you're doing it wrong anyway." When you allow that third-party-you to enter as observer and judge, you will lose all flow and natural rhythm. Touching, and the response to being touched, must be spontaneous. This is difficult for most people. The difficulty dissolves. The more you trust your natural desire for variety, the more often wonder and curiosity will free your actions. You will develop such awe for the other and such joy and lightness of being, that boundaries will dissolve for those moments, minutes or hours. You will enter a place of no time, for you will be in the arms of the eternal moment.

You needn't limit your touching to hands. Every part of your body can be expressive. Remember how babies use their feet as hands? How toddlers rub up against their mother's leg with their whole bodies? I'm mentioning babies and toddlers because they are the uninhibited models of closeness. Watch them. See how they make eye contact without looking away. See how an infant will put your finger into her mouth and suck it, how a baby sucks on a nipple with total involvement. Notice how a young child will touch and taste anything that makes her curious. Be like children. They are natural.

Sometimes I like to run my fingers lightly up and down the back of my lover while he's sliding in and out of my body. The most delicious feeling is having my mouth filled with his tongue at the same time—to feel totally filled at opposite poles of my body. This is extremely passionate if you allow yourself to make sounds and to make and keep eye contact even at that close range. Let your lover see the passion in your face, the surrender, the helpless awe of accepting his or her finest, most intimate gift.

Never lose the awe of that sacred and eternal moment. You should be breathless just recalling the moment in your mind, and very grateful. Bliss is the effortless suspension of breath when the observer, the observed and the act of observation meld into oneness. Eternity is now.

Passion involves awe. When sex becomes mundane it is because you have lost your awe. If that happens, it can be regained. That is the magic. Don't even talk about it with your lover, who is obviously bored as well. Just change it. Changing your actions and attitudes is far more creative than changing your lover. Inspire yourself, and your lover will respond with inspiration.

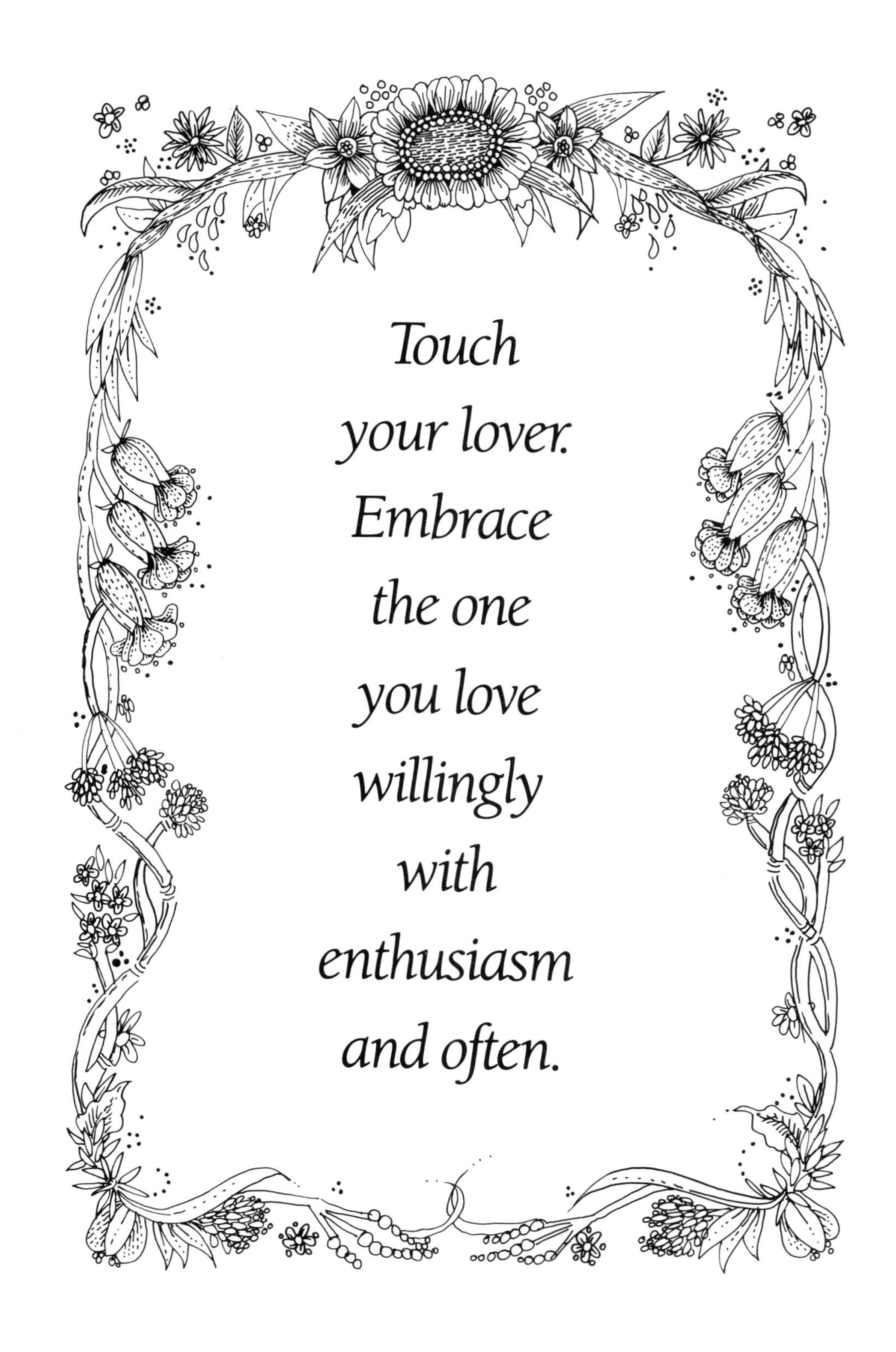
Touch
your lover.
Embrace
the one
you love
willingly
with
enthusiasm
and often.

The Five Senses—Especially Sight

The more sexually mature I've gotten, the more graphic I've become. I love to use all of my senses during sex to enliven my experience and joy. I wondered if this was a natural progression, or if I just was overcoming the engrained taboos of my training. Tattoos are probably easier to get rid of. I was joking earlier about being in the dark—and that would be in more ways than one, obviously. You might be able to make love in the dark, but sex is best in the light. Bringing it into the light—not a blinding light, but a gentle light—makes sex definitely more erotic. Perhaps it's because people are ashamed of their fat or their wrinkles, and perhaps it's just because shame over sex in general has been in-bred for so long that it takes years to overcome our conditioning. I don't really know, but as in the first chapters on discovery, I'd like to challenge you to become more aware of the excitement of sexual vision. This is an attitude as well as an action, and is all-encompassing when integrated into your sexuality. It will change it totally, making you freer, making you more appreciative of your lover's body and your own body, and it definitely will make you more erotic.

As you read, become aware of your inner feelings: acceptance, disgust, shock, whatever awareness hits you, and make a mental note of it, or better yet, make honest notes in the margins. These will be good clues to fearlessly discover your sexual inhibitions.

For some reason men have been given permission to be much more graphic than women. Maybe testosterone is more visual than estrogen. Whatever the reason, men are not ashamed of it. When a woman is graphic rather than demure, she feels she is going against her culture. This is a very serious thing, because still inbred is the feeling of being stoned to death. Anyone who saw or read *Zorba the Greek* knows what I mean: the man walks away but the woman gets stoned. In the fifties the woman was a slut and the man made a conquest. This still prevails in the psyche of many a lover and, needless to say, it is quite threatening, even when thought and not spoken. No woman wants to be thought of as a slut.

Getting older has an advantage. You get to a point where you don't care what people think of you. You know that by living to your own rhythm, your own drummer, you are being true to yourself, so if someone thinks you're loose because of your sexual opinions, so what? The person judging you is probably jealous of your free attitude and would absolutely love to squash it along with the overripe, unused fruit of his or her own sexual orchard. Now you have a choice: to live to the other's standards, or to follow your own heartbeat.

If we didn't have this graphic urge, we never would have invented mirrors, cameras, movies, videos and television. Men are unashamedly graphic sexually. Women should become part of that movement. Acceptance of the excitement of seeing your sexual embrace in the light, seeing the penis erect, seeing your own genitals, and the two sliding together in their sexual dance, seeing the embrace of your mouth on his penis, so close that you can see every vein as well as feel it with your tongue, or his on you, or your hands vibrating to each other's rhythms—these are erotic joys you should not be missing. *It literally is a focus on what you are doing—a visual meditation.* You are using your eyes as an erotic organ. And the sight of this slippery shining sex will turn you on whether you want it to or not.

Now, let's go back to analyze and resolve how you feel about what I just wrote.

I honor your feelings and responses to what I wrote even if I might not agree with them. It took me years to get over all of the sexual repression my mother bred into me from childhood until

I was married. Needless to say, I was not raised with all this freedom of thought.

I remember my mother talking about sex, saying "I couldn't stand the sight of *it*. I never touched it or looked at it. The very thought of it makes me sick." "One time your father wanted to do it like they do to the whores – he wanted to bend me over a chair." She spoke with loathing and disgust. I think there are a lot of men out there who also don't want to look at *it* (meaning female genitals) and they also better get over their squeamishness if they want to be good lovers. That attitude is a total lack of honoring the other. Honoring and valuing the other's body is an act of respect. Lovers are allowing themselves to be so open that the other sees everything. To refuse to look and accept and admire and adore is a sacrilege. Looking, touching, feeling and tasting are acts of wonder and awe. That exciting desire should never leave, and is a permanent act of respect that comes from the lover. If it is not there, the person who receives the slight is damaged, feels ugly, inappropriately open, and resentful. You may as well know the damage you're causing by not honoring *it* with your vision, your hands, your mouth and your awe. Fear of this deep intimacy will ruin sex faster than a speeding bullet. Perhaps it will shed light on the matter to understand why women might be shy of showing their genitals freely to their lover with pride. *Pudendum*, the medical term for a woman's vulva, translates to: *that which one should be ashamed of.*

If you felt disgust or shock at what I've been talking about, you too would be wise to remember your parents' attitudes about sex and the actual organs we hide. I would rather think I am covering them because they are special than hiding them because I think they're ugly. If you have a hard time looking at first, do it gradually. Get used to it, but keep stretching yourself to remember to be graphic. As you work out the kinks in your sexual armoring, you will start to enjoy and become more erotic, you will lose your shame as easily as ice melts in warm water. If you are female, you will notice your vaginal juices flowing more copiously, a very healthy sign psychologically and physically. Genitals are beautiful and they are all different. Look at them as openly as you would look at your lover's face. Let your attitude be open and admiring, curious and generous.

Orgasmic Masturbation

Masturbation is an ugly word. The etymology is Latin and means to practice self-abuse. It is commonly held to be derived from 'manustuprare'–'to defile with the hand'.

Actually, masturbating is normal, according to most sex therapists, even though it is considered perverse and sinful by religious fundamentalists. It feels good, and even very young children will stroke their hands over their genitals, at least until a puritanical parent whacks them. I remember my daughter as a very young child putting my hand too low on her stomach to mean much else. I remember responding, "That's okay for you to do, but not okay for mommies to do for you." Hopefully, in that sentence, I was washing away the harm my own mother had done to me by beating me for her paranoid fears of masturbation.

As an adult, masturbation is usually accepted, at least in this day and age, especially if one has no sex partner. The pressure build-up is far from healthy if not released. The yogis have a way of recirculating their energy, at least for men. But most people seem to need a physical release for desire to clear the system. Orgasm is normal and healthy.

When one is finally rid of the embarrassment of talking about masturbation or performing it, it can become a beautiful sex tool between partners. Masturbating the other is a highly charged sex act. And masturbating the self openly for the other is also a highly charged sex act. It takes quite a bit of self-acceptance to reach this point. To open oneself this much is a trust issue, and most people have difficulty reaching such a relaxed and open state. Practice again is the key to becoming unselfconscious.

One of my most sensual experiences is having my partner over my breasts masturbating to climax. It is visual, aural, a place where I can inhale the excitement as well as the scent of his body. I can see his ecstasy through his face, his tensed muscles, his perspiration, his muscular movement, his breath becoming short and his voice becoming distinctly animalistic. It is wild, exciting and furiously sexual. I love it.

Obviously men like to see women masturbate as well. Especially when a man has his face between a woman's thighs, it is a tactile, intimate and sensual act, where his tongue and mouth are sucking her fingers as well as her labia. A woman's touching herself during sex is poetic and takes the passivity out of just lying there. A woman can be sexually active even while being the receiving partner.

Stroking oneself as well as the other is a more than acceptable act of passion. It can be gentle or firm, very slow or very fast, having the rhythm of whatever mood you are in. Again, it is creating your own poem or painting, and each time it is different, new, varied and wonderful. It is an act of freedom and acceptance, and it is truly exciting for your partner.

When I am giving my lover oral sex, I use my hands and fingers as well, so that it is a combination of masturbation with fellatio. That gives me more latitude to be creative. But sometimes I feel a more powerful urge to masturbate him hard, so I can watch his muscles tighten in ripples from overwhelming sensation. If you ask your lover to masturbate for you, you can see how he or she does it, and then you can learn technique that pleases. You can do other things as well, but then you know how your partner likes to reach climax when he or she is finally ready.

The area should be slippery rather than dry, and saliva is the best sexual lubricant.

Masturbating another to orgasm or watching them masturbate to orgasm is an extremely intimate act, probably more difficult to accept than intercourse, in the sense of overcoming shyness. It is more open and riskier. You will gain much by opening up to this seriously exciting exchange of sexual energy. It is very tactile, and one of the nicest sexual gifts you can give to your partner. Expand your horizon and try it.

A word to the wise: Endurance is important. It is not kind to stop in an untimely fashion because your muscles can't keep up with your passion. No matter how difficult this is, you can't let your partner down when climax is close or there will never be trust again. If you are practicing and don't think you'll last, let him or her know you might not be able to finish off that way, and then there will be no expectations of fulfillment from that specific act. When the passion is hottest, the receiving partner might spontaneously change to the act he or she wants to climax with.

Masturbating another is an art. Treat your partner now with the awe and adulation he or she deserves. This act is about honoring the other in heated passion and desire. Climax this way is extremely powerful and fulfilling.

Erotic feelings with your lover should be expressed freely and passionately.

Fellatio as a Master Stroke

You might be thinking, "Just another intellectual book about overcoming your hangups. When is she going to get to the nitty-gritty?" To get to the hot stuff, folks, you have to get rid of your hangups first. But, you're right, now the book heats up.

In thinking about all of this sexual stuff, it occurred to me that the English language is extremely unpoetic. 'Blow job.' Can you just see that—a chapter on how to give a blow job. Giving head the way he likes best. Oral sex. Fellatio. Really, can't we invent some better terms? Or, do the terms reflect our ignorance and distaste for sex, our puritanical and condemning attitudes to sensuality for the sake of pleasure? This may be quite true, unfortunately, and when we reclaim our sensual natures, we may discover new and inviting terms. Until then, I have to use the terms we have coined.

How do you give a good blow job, ladies? Ladies don't do that, women do. Sensual, excited, deliciously uninhibited women do it.

I was in Las Vegas for a book convention a few years back, and a comedian from Chicago asked the women in the audience how many of them thought a man should fix things around the house—you know, be somewhat handy so you didn't have to buy new things just because something broke. Every woman in the audience raised her hand, including me. Then, while everyone was making just enough noise, he said under his breath, "And you should learn to give good head." I think he speaks for a lot of men.

I wanted to see how I stacked up as far as giving really good head is concerned, so I rented some X-rated videos to see if I could learn something. That in itself was pushing my limits of courage—to be in the video store finding a movie and actually asking for it. I have to say it rates right up there with asking for condoms, or carrying sanitary napkins up to the counter when you are 12 years old. I didn't quite have the courage to actually go into the X-rated section—I copped out and just read the book of titles. Then I finally just asked them to give me what was most popular. After watching many of them, I decided the femmes fatales could teach me nothing. I would just have to trust myself and go with my own sexual instincts. But at least I had the courage to check it out. It did confirm my belief that you have to enjoy it a lot to be very effective.

Practice. Practice. Practice. What makes you good at everything, including sex, is practice, discovery, experimenting, and more practice. But it must be done with a sense of joy and playfulness, in the not-so-passionate moments as well, when you can giggle and be casual, experimenting and overcoming shyness at saying what you like and what feels good. In more passionate moments the words should be abandoned to sexual words and sounds entirely. We have to teach ourselves and be each other's teachers. It may be only, "That's so good. That. Do that. I love it." Or, "More gently...like that...". Make sure your tone of voice is encouraging and not critical.

During oral sex, saliva is going to be one of your finest tools of delight, for the slipperier you can make your actions, the more wild you will drive him. You will notice as you practice (and I am sure you will have a willing volunteer) your saliva will become substantially richer both in quantity and quality. Use it. Let your own slippery salivation turn you on as well as your lover.

A reminder: You have ten fingers and two palms, cheeks, lips, a tongue with muscles that move, breasts with nipples, and a throat that goes all the way to your stomach. Not that you will go that far, but don't think of your mouth as ending at the epiglottus. It goes farther back than that, and this is why you have to practice: to remove any claustrophobic fears you may have; to desensitize your gag reflex; to realize that you can find a way to breathe enough, especially so you don't stop when he is really getting into it and near orgasm—if it is your understanding that's where the climax will take place. Practice will give you confidence and knowledge of your own physical capacities.

When he starts getting really passionate, he will move more. Instead of letting that frighten you, go with it. Get more turned on yourself. It it's too much for you, slow him down so that only you are moving. Feel the end of his cock in your mouth, with the texture so different from the shaft. Appreciate that. Adore his body, his organ with all of its pulsing veins and ridges. Explore it curiously, watching it whenever you can, touching it with every convenient area of your body, and especially your palms and fingers as your mouth, throat and tongue slide upward. And when your mouth slides toward his body once more, slip those ever-moving wet fingers all around his balls and the sensitive skin in the area. If you get tired and need to rest, keep your hands and fingers active and move the head of his cock onto one of your breasts. While your hand keeps slowly active, occasionally licking to keep the shaft of his penis wet and slippery, your mouth and throat muscles will have a chance to recover, but you will not need to stop your actions and ruin his exquisite build-up. Keep the feeling of flow. Keep letting your saliva juices flow, and as you do, your vaginal juices will flow copiously as well. Think of your own succulent body that he will soon enter with joyous passion.

Again, if you have fear, or are just learning, ask your partner to lie still and not push into you. If you have control of how deeply he enters, you will feel more secure and be able to go at your own pace.

One thing that kept me so long from giving really great head to my partner was the fear he would come in my mouth. The man I had lived with for eight years had such an unpleasantly bitter and lasting flavor that I never really did it well when I knew he was getting near climax. When a man comes in a woman's mouth with no forewarning, she may feel tricked. First, if it's before he satisfies her, his passion will likely abate so he won't take care of her as well. Oral sex should fall within the term of foreplay, unless it is understood otherwise. Communication should be clear.

I learned a lot by asking my close girlfriends about how they handled oral sex. My best girlfriend was the one who gave me the biggest clue on the bad flavor and difficult consistency issue. She told me to position the head of his cock far back in my throat, and that way there would be no sensation of taste or texture. With practice, the back of my throat has gotten farther and farther back, so now my lover can enjoy almost his full length in my throat at his peak experience. The other good news is that you don't have to use your swallowing muscles to swallow, and you won't gag. Your esophagus literally is an involuntary muscle when it needs to be and works on its own. I'm telling you all this so you become expert at this with less practice and experimenting time than it took me. However, I still suggest you practice often—especially if you've just quit smoking! Practicing is essential to desensitize the gag reflex, which will be very sensitive at first.

As you get more comfortable with using your hands and fingers as well as your mouth during fellatio, you can get into the many variations you will discover as your passions flow. A good lover knows she never makes love exactly the same way twice. She might remember what she did that was pleasurable to her lover, but it will not be done exactly the same way. It will be done with the same sexual style, but not quite the same, because as each painting takes on different hues and colors, so, too, does sex. Vary your sexual brush strokes with your mood.

One really fun variation is lifting and firmly holding the man's legs, like they like to lift ours, so his whole genital area is available to you. This also satisfies his passive fantasies of being dominated by a masterful, sexual woman. Then, use your tongue and lips all over his testicles both tickling, and then with copious saliva, sliding your lips and tongue and eventually your full face back and forth over the entire area in a light, all-encompassing movement of your cheeks and face. Lose yourself in the pleasure of feeling your whole face on his most sensitive area, making a point to pay especial attention to the hard and wonderfully sensitive engorged area that's inaccessible any other way. Any shyness you may feel at the beginning will dissolve, for this is a truly magnificent feeling for both of you. At this point, a gentle fingering or tongue flickering or sliding over his clean anal area is a thrill—sometimes called analingus—and if you're not sure of the cleanliness of the area, just use your fingertip and a lot of saliva to gently penetrate his anal passageway without using your tongue. Just an inch inward you will feel a soft area on the stomach side of the passageway. This is the prostate gland, and if you massage it gently as you're sucking on and stroking his penis, it will bring him a most unusual orgasm, where the semen literally flows out of him rather than coming in squirts. What I say is based on not having gash-threatening fingernails. So if you have them, and your man trusts you enough to let them near his groin, you'll have to develop your own technique. Use a rhythm that is commensurate with the rhythm your mouth is using to move down on him. It will come naturally. The combination of sucking on him and moving your finger gently inside is so thrilling because the prostate is so sexually sensitive. Make sure your finger and the area are very slippery. Of course, hygiene should have been taken care of earlier. Move very cautiously, making sure you feel no resistance of skin or muscle. If you do, stop immediately. Wait for some communication for continuation or withdrawal. When you do at any point remove your finger, withdraw very slowly. Always make sure your saliva is acting as a lubricant. If you have long nails. Don't do this. Your index finger, which is the one you will be using, or your thumb, depending on your position, should have a very short nail and should be very smooth. I hear that it is a delightful and unusual sensation, and from my end of it, it is quite exciting bringing my lover off this way.

Another way I particularly enjoy is when I am on my back and my lover is kneeling over my chest, leaning forward on hands and knees. The position is especially visually erotic, and the angle of entry is superb. If you don't feel comfortable holding your head up by your own strength, slip a soft pillow under your head, without too much lift. This is an extremely hot position, and the body feelings which are aroused from it are all-consuming. This position may be too difficult for beginners. Make sure your lover is high enough over you so he doesn't smother you. This is not a position for large people, unfortunately. The stronger your muscles, the better. The view is intense.

My third favorite position for giving oral sex is having my lover stand while I slide down the front of his body, carrying with me his belt, pants and shorts. It's best to slip them entirely off. While I feel the back of his legs with my hands and fingers, I like to tease him a little by kissing and licking his stomach and inner thighs to build his intensity. This is also an extremely erotic position, with your one knee down and one knee up, especially with lace-top stockings and garters. If you at all are inclined to enjoy Victoria's Secret, this is the time. In any case, it is a very exciting position for me.

A favorite morning position for a quieter passion is face to face. Lying this way, slide your softly awakening body down slowly towards the foot of the bed stopping at a perfect position for his penis to enter your mouth at exactly the angle most comfortable for you. He may be awake, or he may be just on the verge, so be very quiet and very in tune with his awakening process. Be careful to be firm yet gentle in your motions because a light touch will tickle, and you want to arouse not annoy. This is an angle that allows for the deepest penetration at your own pace. His sleepiness will invite him to be somewhat still, and your own motions can be self-controlled because he is likely to enjoy being passive at this hour. Use this to your advantage to practice taking him deeper into your relaxed throat. Go very slowly, even to the point of slow-motion smoothness. Early is quiet. Your gentleness in passion can be overwhelmingly sensual. Use this time to create. I doubt if you will encounter any resistance to this particularly expressive sexual stroke, even if it wakes him up from a sound sleep.

Another very stimulating position is to lie on your back with your male partner kneeling at your side, so while your mouth and fingers caress his wonderful penis, he too can be caressing your sexual organs with his hand. There is something to be said for mutuality, especially with oral sex. There are many ways where both partners can be active with oral sex, although it certainly feels very special to be receptive without condition. When the moments are right for this mutual-type of sharing, the partner receiving oral sex can reciprocate quite nicely by using his or her hands and mouth to stimulate the other. As in intercourse, there are many ways to achieve this depending on your body types and physical condition. The issue, of course, is to be creative and unashamedly bold with your imagination.

When you are actively satisfying your partner orally, remember to use the rest of your body in your actions. Get the feeling that you have when you dance and your whole body is movement without any solid limitations of gravity or structure.

Whatever pleases you, and whatever pleases your lover will be the best way for you. These suggestions should only get you thinking and creating in your own special ways.

One small note, if you find your mouth is too small or your lover is too large for your mouth without possibly hurting him with your teeth, slip the tip of your index finger between your front teeth and your man's penis. Your teeth will be buffered by your nail so as not to hurt your finger, and your finger will act as a lever and cushion for him. If even this doesn't work, you have a really high-class problem and I'm sure you'll figure out some creative solution!

Good oral sex is one of the greatest pleasures one can give to another. And the only way to do it well is to do it with total absorption, as though it were the only thing in the world you wanted to do, ever. As though morning, noon and night could not possibly be enough time to give as much pleasure as you really want to give. As though the entire world could fall away and that would be all to be left, just you two in the slippery, hot embrace of oral passion. It can be just that—you can wish it would be all morning, noon and night. That feeling will show, and it will be incredibly thrilling and a smashing compliment. It can be the most fun of anything on earth, and it is tantamount to heavenly bliss. It is not a sacrifice to prove anything, it is rather a sacrifice of honor. Remember that the word 'sacrifice' means an offering. Be honored at being able to do this lovely, sensual act. Do it well with the master's touch. Do it with reverence. Remember the sacred in this special act, and honor the other as though he were godlike. For that's what he is, and that too is what you are. There are no others. You are the archetypal images of love.

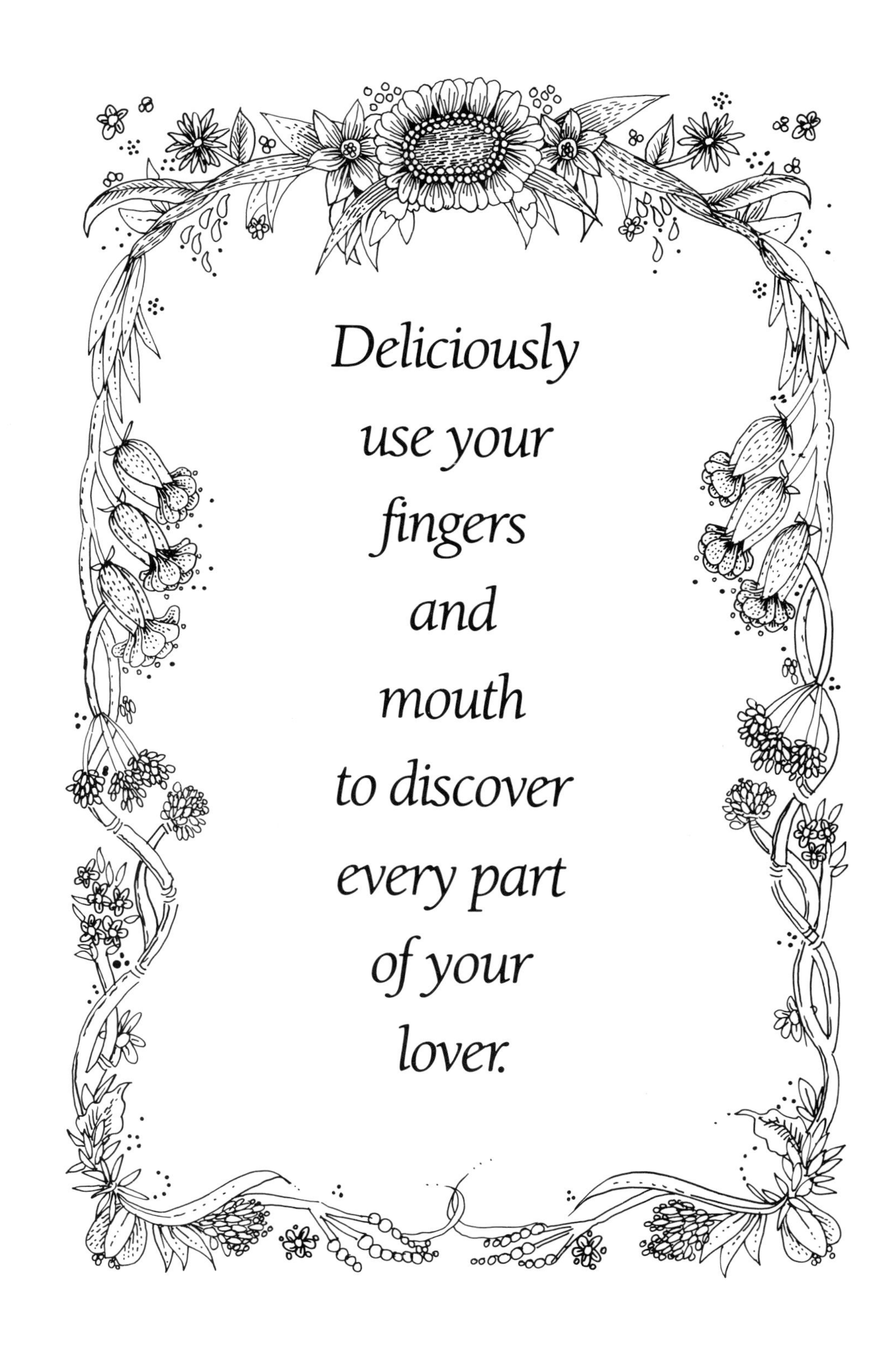

Deliciously
use your
fingers
and
mouth
to discover
every part
of your
lover.

What Do Women Like?

This chapter is about what sexually oriented women like. First, women in general are usually extremely romantic. All of the images you can muster about story-book romance truly please a woman. Compliments about her eyes, breasts, and legs, with heavy or not-so-heavy meaning, flowers, cards, and especially phone calls are very important in validating her importance in your life.

A woman also likes to make eye contact over the dinner table as you tenderly touch her hand and she likes gentle touches on the shoulder or back as you stand or walk side by side. Even little notes and cards. A woman needs to be wooed.

Appropriate advances even of this soft a nature come most naturally with time, and are inappropriate without prior psychological intimacy. There are, of course, exceptions, and timing is important. Personal interactions of more than a friendly nature are never appropriate in the workplace. Restrain yourself at all times in business. Women need to be taken seriously, and sexual advances or innuendoes in the workplace are very demeaning, and can even cost you your job or more. Whether or not you agree, the advice remains.

Wooing or courting a woman is a necessary psychological preface. It follows that a man who moves too fast out of bed usually moves too fast once he's *in* bed. A man who eats too fast usually falls into the same category. There's another good reason not to move too fast in getting her to bed. Sometimes the first time isn't the best, most especially if you're so revved up you come too soon, and if a woman feels you're a bad lover, you likely won't get another chance. If you take the time to woo her (not faking who you are, but getting to know her gently), and I don't mean the first night only, your personality will have had a greater chance to come out positively. She'll feel closer to you, so it will be a lot more personal, and if you're not the best the first time, you will have a second chance, we hope. But maybe a few pointers will help you so you won't need to redeem yourself.

Men might think they are considerate and truly caring because they ask the woman if she orgasmed. I'm only speaking from my own experience, but whenever a man keeps asking me, it turns me off. It brings me out of my reverie right back to square one. Sex is a crescendo, and verbal questions can be disruptive. This may depend upon your partner, but making sure you take time to satisfy her will eliminate the need to keep asking her. As a man, how do you feel if a woman keeps asking, "Did you come? Did you come? Did you come?" I feel like I'm on some kind of performance check, or the man wants me to hurry. I think that's why we all fake orgasm sometimes. We feel that the man feels we're taking too long, and we feel under pressure to hurry. If a man has satisfied me orally before he enters, which I prefer, he doesn't have to ask. I think many women would like a man orally to bring them to orgasm at least once before he enters. Unless a woman is extremely noiseless, it should be apparent, but perhaps not. If it's okay with her that you ask, try not to make her feel rushed, or that will turn her off. Learn the things that make her orgasm and do them so you won't have to ask, and encourage her noises so that you have expressive wordless feedback, unless she herself wants to verbalize her feelings. Coax her in sexy ways. Find out what she likes by taking your time in the process of her build-up, then use those techniques to tantalize her to orgasm. The slower the build-up, the greater the intensity of her orgasm will be. The greater your enjoyment, the greater hers will be.

I was married very young with only a little petting experience behind me. I made the terrible mistake of believing society's edict of staying a virgin. The man I married was nearly a virgin, but qualified because he was so scared in bed. Now I didn't know that at the time, of course. Maybe female virginity—you notice male virginity is not particularly admired by society—is basically a patriarchal edict. I've since suspected it was practiced so a woman can't compare a man's performance, or because we are considered merchandise. We're just things, and we're either new or we're used. In any case, my well-intentioned husband could not get more than ten strokes in (five if I gave him oral sex first) before the moment of his climax. This went on for months, and finally, shy newlywed as I was, I asked him to help me after the fact to be satisfied. So, boringly, since I'm sure he wanted to go to sleep by then, he ineptly stroked me, *quite* ineptly, I might add. Then would stop because he fell asleep, then abruptly resume his staccato hurry-up-and-come movement because he'd wake up and feel guilty, then stop again, until I finally just pushed his hand away and rolled over in pain. When I told him what I liked, and the movements that turned me on, he got very angry and told me not to tell him how to make love.

I put up with this treatment for seven long and horny years, faithfully, and then seven more not quite so faithfully. I'd succumb to my human nature about once a year, then feel guilty for another year until horniness overtook me once again. I'm sure my condition was stamped in red on my forehead. A big red 'H'. Today a woman would not put up with that. And then again I wonder how many women do put up with that even today. So I have been thinking about my past best lovers and worst lovers and what the difference was, so that I could share it and save at least a few people some pain. A marriage without good sex does not easily survive, so whether you're single or married this *does* apply to you.

When I started thinking about what my best past lovers did so well, the point was so clear I was stunned. The best lovers made certain that I orgasmed at least once before even entering my body. By that time I was so wet and crazy with passion I'm sure the experience was much more intensely enjoyable for them as well.

Other points were: the very best ones still made out on the couch long enough to drive me wild before gently pulling me toward the bedroom. Then they took off my clothes very slowly while still kissing me, clothes which were already hanging limply down my bare shoulders and breasts. It is very sensual to have someone else take off your clothes. No one is in that big of a hurry. It is incredibly sensual, especially if you caress the skin as you erotically remove the clothes. Take enough time to do it really well—it's worth the delayed gratification. It's even fun just to think about it, isn't it?

The best lovers thought of my body as delicious fruit, and gently moved their lips all over my face, neck and shoulders, sliding down to my breasts and nipples, slowly working down my trembling torso to my pubic area. The delight was apparent, and they stayed there. I could tell from their sounds and movements they loved it. We'll talk later about techniques, but the point here is *they transmitted in body language that they loved it*. And they stayed with me in my build-up until I climaxed at least once before attempting intercourse.

The best lovers made good eye contact throughout lovemaking. If it's difficult for you, practice. It will help you in your daily life as well as in your sex life. You can really get close with your eyes, which are the opening to your heart. Even at face-to-face range it is intensely provocative.

The best lovers continually erotically kissed my mouth most

of the time. The wet lips and tongue are wonderful instruments of delight. Don't neglect the oral sensualness of your mouths together all throughout your lovemaking. While you are genitally intertwined you still have a lot of leeway for your arms, hands, fingers and mouth.

The best lovers had a firm touch. Firm, but not heavy, and very smooth, not jerky. It gave me the feeling of their being relentless, which is very thrilling for me. So their feeling of self-assurance was obvious, and their desire to be right there for me was also obvious. When a man has a wish-washy touch, it's almost repulsive. You keep feeling that he wishes it were over, or he's afraid of you. Being tentative about your touch is frustrating. Go with it in confidence and assurance. Unfortunately, this inability of assurance probably comes from the inside, and is a symptom of your self-esteem. Even if you're just beginning to discover your sexuality, believe that you are okay.

The best lovers could be passive as well as assertive, and were comfortable in both situations. I always feel like a sexual goddess when I'm astride—not overpowering, but powerfully giving. This position is not a power trip, believe me.

The best lovers were turned on to all parts of my body and did not just fixate on my genitals. No woman wants a man who thinks sex is merely a ramrod affair.

The best lovers I've ever had treated me as though I were sexy and let me know how much I turned them on. The worst lovers I've ever had treated me as though *they* were sexy and wanted verbal reassurance of how much they turned *me* on, giving me no feedback in return.

My very best lovers brought out the freedom in me to go beyond my past limits. I literally could growl and moan and scream in my animal nature, and make human crying sounds because of the depth of my passion and openness. Feeling that free involves a great acceptance. I now believe sounding while fucking is one of the biggest turn-ons there is. Unfortunately, some of my best lovers did not make noise. I think this was an inhibition on their part, and I'll tell you why I think it is wonderful to let yourself go in this way.

I had a relationship with a man who was not necessarily my best lover, but he made me climax with him during intercourse with no foreplay whatsoever, every time (after the initial getting-to-know phase). I ended up living with him for eight years—and still it was steadily satisfying sexually. I think this is why he could bring me off so easily: he moved extremely sensually. I knew he was not worried about my orgasm, so neither was I. I'm telling you, "Did you come? Did you come?" can really pull a girl down from the mountain fast. Anyway, his buildup was slow and steady. I could feel from the inside his body rising sexually, and it felt as though he were a locomotive pulling me in his wake—a deeply physical surrender for me which was inwardly joyous and totally freeing. I would feel like our genitals were glued together and had a life of their own irrespective of him and me. My vaginal muscles would literally grip his penis, so that instead of sliding in and out, my whole inner body moved with him. I could see us from the inside as though my eyes were in my vagina. I could put my entire consciousness in my genitals and be them. If I didn't come first, I could not stop myself once he started. Within nanoseconds I would get there to be with him as he climaxed, because he groaned and moaned the whole time in such passionate wild joy that the sounds resonated throughout my entire body and brought me at once to the highest peaks of splendor. It was otherworldly. And he hardly used any technique by that time because of lazy living with each other over the years.

Only in the morning would he roll me over, and if not then, not at all until the next morning. No nights, no afternoons and no quickie surprises. Sounds dull, doesn't it? Yet this man had the incredible ability to throw my body into paroxysms of orgasm within minutes of entry because how he let his body totally uninhibitedly take over, and was able to move like a panther and scream like one when he came. Now a man like that can get away with a lot, and he did. He probably always will. Like Eddie Murphy's routine in *Raw* when he said, to paraphrase, "Once she says 'woo woo woo' man, you've got her!" Don't rely on that, however.

The best lovers do not change what they are doing, if they know they are being responded to. Variety can at times be a mistake in bed. I don't mean be boring. I mean that if you feel the woman is really responding to a certain movement or combination of movements that you're making, either the way you are stroking her with your hand, or some other rhythm you are using genitally, or a certain way you are moving your mouth on her clit, don't stop. Body language is very obvious. Trust it. Once you start to trust yourself, it will become even more obvious. When you get good at self-trust, you'll wonder why you ignored it for so long. You will feel an electric charge of connection that's being made, like an electrical glue. If you stop or change at this moment, she may slide all the way down to the bottom and have to start all over again. And if she's disgusted at you for stopping, it may be all over for her at that point, especially during oral sex. It is much more difficult physically for a woman to give good oral sex for an extended period than it is for a man to give it to a woman. She has to learn much more muscle control even than you do, so do her a favor and learn to last. Don't quit when it feels good to her because you don't want to develop your tongue or your sucking muscles, or you are impatient for your own orgasm. You take longer than you think to reach orgasm, so cut us some slack. Be a sport and go to the finish. If you want to keep getting good head from her, you'll have to give it to her, as well.

Good lovers *take time.*

I was thinking about how and why things feel good to me—certain movements, etc., and what keeps me creative. It's the curious little kid part we use in discovery our whole lives, the part that never stops, and if it does, we become boring people.

Giving your woman good oral sex deserves a whole chapter, so read on.

Giving a Woman Oral Sex

The clit is a wonderful thing. When a woman is aroused, it swells, and when you spread her thighs and look therein, you will discover the most magical flower in the world, right before your very eyes, wanting to be admired, waiting to bloom, oozing out delicious and slippery moisture to invite you even deeper. It's a flower whose essence you can enter, as every bee tries to emulate, but cannot in the way that you can. It's a flower whose mystery you will never fully unravel. It will never lose its beauty or mystery, and if you treat it right, it will bloom even more fully.

The clit, which you may not know, goes all the way around the vaginal opening like a cloak. What you see of it is its flowering bud. The most sensitive part becomes engorged to be more available to the touch. This is a gift, to both you and your female lover. If you do not visually love to experience this part of a woman's many-faceted sexual body, it is because of society's training. I suggest you read more books and talk to friends until your fear of this wonderful flower leaves you, until you can totally delve into it with all the delight of a discoverer. If you do not overcome your aversion, you will be missing one of life's finest gifts. And you are destined to lose what you cherish most—the person attached to it. Don't kid yourself, it is that important to a woman. It is especially insulting if you expect her to give you oral sex, yet you won't reciprocate.

You will never give good oral sex if you don't love it. You can do all the right things on the outside, but if your inside has any reservation whatsoever, and you can't truly and immensely enjoy giving a woman cunnilingus, no amount of physical manipulation will be satisfying to her. Your aversion to her body will be apparent to her. If she does climax, it will be from a fantasy, not from you. If you can be satisfied with a detached attitude, she can't be, so she will attach to something, even if it is a fantasy about someone else.

Of course it is expected that a woman should have good hygiene if she wants to be desirable. Her genitalia are an enclosed area and should be cared for especially well, washing immediately before sex even if she's recently bathed. Important things deserve good care. Jokes about a woman smelling like fish are not very funny to a woman. Men should also take care with their hygiene as well, especially if they like to receive oral sex. They are not odor- and germ-free either, and should be aware of that. To be safe, the anal area should be extremely clean. A therapist I know felt discriminated against when she read this chapter. Her comment was, "Men who don't like eating a woman use that as a smokescreen. A man who really loves it enjoys the taste." I don't particularly agree with her, but that's a matter of opinion. So, this is for all you guys who are squeamish. Don't expect to receive good oral sex if you don't give it. No 68's—"You do me and I'll owe you one."

We are not talking about quickies here, so if you are worried about scent or cleanliness, whisper in her ear to wait for you, lick her ear or breast to keep her interest, or slip her hand onto her genitals, and quietly slip out of bed. Get a warm, damp cloth and dry towel to cleanse and dry her, and slip back into bed. Spread her legs sensually. Open them really wide to enjoy the view. Make nice noises or give words of appreciation at her vulvic beauty, and sensually looking at her, let her know that looking at her that way really turns you on. Then stroke her gently clean with the cloth, and pat her dry with the towel. Wrap the cloth in the towel, lay it on the floor, and *voilà!* there you are, fresh and clean just for you. If you're squeamish.

And now she is even more ready, because what you just did is a turn-on, done smoothly. She feels really primed now, and any reservation either of you had about her cleanliness is wiped away in a caring and sensitive ritual. Now, with her body opened in total surrender, she feels the thrill of her energy pattern reversing, flowing downward toward your mouth. If done with an expert's touch, she allows her whole energy flow to be pulled from her, like a long, continual sexual string. If her legs are up, the sexual energy goes up. If she is over your face, her sexual energy will flow downwards. She is sacrificing her body to you in a most splendid way, and it is exemplified in the reversal of her energy flow, which normally flows up her spine toward her head rather than downward. She feels you sucking her energy from her very depths, and she knows that only in allowing that to happen will she also receive. The more profoundly this act is performed – that is, with awe, attention and focus – the more effective will be its results. Do not hurry. Keep your focus and intensity. Don't ask her questions that she has to respond to. Let her non-verbal responses be your feedback. Picture her energy being pulled into your mouth like a sexual nectar. The longer you take, the more gently you move and the more fully you concentrate, the more potent will be her buildup and climax.

This is when you must trust your intuition to know what is turning her on. Whatever you do, keep doing it rhythmically once she has entered your grasp and you feel her mesmerized to your mouth. Do not go randomly from flicking to licking to sucking to poking to lapping. Sometimes, especially when building up tension to orgasm, changing technique is extremely disruptive, and, though it might feel 'good', it won't do the job. Different strokes should be enjoyed at the beginning of your oral sex, not the end. Slow, steady, intentional. Let your intuition tell you what to do, not your mind. Trust your inner feelings, not your computer chatter. *Never blow air into her vaginal cavity. It is physically dangerous*. However, if you desire, blow your breath gently from your lips on the outside, blowing very softly. Your gentle, hot breath will drive her crazy. If you put your lips around her clit area, make them fit like a glove to keep the suction. Suck gently and firmly, again keeping your whole mind focused on your action. Intention will keep her drawn into your spell. She may seem frozen to the spot with no movement because her body is so intensely surrendering to you. Her whole consciousness will be in the part of her body that is getting gently sucked. It is not because she is not responding, but because she is responding so totally internally. It should seem to her at this point that you will do this all night. That is the feeling you must impart. And the paradox of this is that the more she feels this, the sooner she'll climax because of her surety that you will satisfy her totally. Don't talk now, just feel with your intuition what you are doing. Keep your intention pointedly focused on her genitals. Don't change position if possible while tension is building. If you change anything in your movements, do it only as your spirit directs, and change it slowly, within the context of what you are doing. Keep focusing your intent. She will follow that energy. You are controlling her, and her energy will flow with your control. She wants to be controlled now. She needs it. This is control as a healthy action. Go with it. Stay with your intent even more strongly now. As your body tells you, you may vary if the voice is the voice of the sexual dance, not the voice of your ego saying "Am I good? Am I good?". If your voice is the sexual intuitive dance, you may vary your movement if you change smoothly with a comma, never a dot dot dot.

As you are sucking on her, her sensations can be accentuated when one finger is gently inserted into her vagina, almost without pause, and ever-so-subtly. More than one finger can cause pain, and any possibility of this will cause her to withdraw from her splendor. In this case, less is more. You are trying to slip her into an exotic ecstasy almost without her knowing. Don't have rough edges or untrimmed nails, or it's over. And since you don't always know when you are going to be the world's best lover called to action, keep them trimmed and smooth. Slowly and gently sliding your finger in and out, as you continue to gently suck on her exposed clitoral area, will be total delight for her, believe me. She might reach an almost immediate climax. If and when she does, keep the movement going even after you think she's finished. The orgastic feelings in a woman are like water, they keep flowing generously for a long time, lasting a while even after they seem to come to rest. Stop when she moves as though she wants you to stop, or says something. More is better than less at this point, more meaning longer.

Also, don't forget the famous 'G' spot–if you bend your finger towards her stomach side once it's inserted, it hits almost exactly on the spot. Wiggling vertically and/or horizontally is a wonderful feeling for her.

I keep emphasizing intent, and you may wonder what I mean by that. I speak about focus in the same regard. When you put all of your energy into one point, the power and focus of that energy is transmitted to the other. That is when and only when she will feel that magnetic pull of her energy into your mouth and finger. That is what will ultimately bring her to climax, no matter what your technique, providing you are smooth.

After she has orgasmed fully, if you are very close to your own climax at this point–I can assure you this may turn you on as much as it's turning her on–entry into her vaginal cavity with your engorged penis would not be a bad idea. If you need to renew your erection, or if you want to hold off having intercourse for awhile (and the better you get the more prolonged your lovemaking can become), you might want to have her put her full, wet mouth around your penis now. Being so totally grateful to you for what you have just given her, she should be really responsive to giving you pleasure orally as well. If you think you might come in her mouth, give her the option of intercourse if she would rather, or coming on her body so she can see you. Even if you end up not performing intercourse at this point, because she is already so satisfied, chances are she will not mind. She should be very willing right now to give to you totally and without reservation. While she performs this delicious magical act on your eager body, sound the things that feel good to you now. Give her the satisfaction of knowing how great this feels. Make your uninhibited sounds of pleasure, and that will give her signposts as to what movements turn you on more than other movements. That may vary from time to time, so she needs this feedback in order to give you the highest ecstasy. If you want to share words, share words, but don't ask questions! You can see how any answers will be awkward! Also, questions will distract her focus, taking away from her own intent. It is okay just to lie there and take without giving now. Don't feel impelled by the 'Am I good?' voice to perform more feats. You truly have satisfied her for awhile, and now it's your turn to receive. Take it, unless you're absolutely impelled by that inner voice to do something else. But make sure it's not your ego speaking. It is her turn now to take your energy and body into her mouth, to pull you into the web of ecstasy, the irreversible track, with the power of a locomotive engine pulling you relentlessly toward the hot, wet tunnel, spewing its smoke wildly from its hot stack, transmitting the energy into movement and realization. Go for it!

Fantasies and Phone Sex

Learning how to speak erotically will increase your sexual vocabulary in more ways than verbal. Sometimes words are all you will have—and, done right, will be very satisfying for both you and your lover. Not being able to be erotic on the phone will limit your contact to only the physical. In today's world, we are accessible by phone more often than we are accessible in person. Phone sex is fun, and extremely erotic. A good fantasy on the phone is one of the more exciting forms of sex. It is not deviant. From the ads on late-night television, it would appear sleezy; however, done right, it can be very specially intimate and bonding for a couple in a healthy relationship. It is not meant as a deviant tool for lonely, mentally unbalanced people. Because deviant people may use this form of sex does not mean the *form itself* is deviant.

You may have glossed over 'that' part of the book because it was uncomfortable to you. Dirty words, you think. They are not bad—they are erotic, sensual, and are fun to say when they are appropriate and when judgment is lifted. So, again, look into your attitudes and find out why you think sexual words are objectionable. If you do not want to change your opinion, that's okay, too. Don't have phone sex. But if you are open enough to read on, it will help long-distance relationships a great deal. And it isn't necessary to use sex talk if that is objectionable to you. You can be inviting, loving, and caring with softer words if that is more comfortable to you than harder words. Society has banned sex words—that's one reason to be frightened about using them. However, when they are limited to your own healthy relationship, in your own private conversation—if you don't use a portable phone because no portable phone conversation is private—they are appropriately acceptable. Nowhere are there written rules that say these words are improper when used properly, so to speak. It was terribly difficult for me to write 'those words' when I started this book. You know, the 'uck' words. I didn't use them all the time, because this book is not pornography. It is sexual philosophy and psychology as well as a practicum of some techniques. But I thought, "I won't be real if I don't use them sometimes. And if I can't be real, how can they be?" These are the words you use during sex. If used too often, they become irritating and meaningless. If never used, sex can lose its punctuation. A balance is necessary to blend the physical with the spiritual, erotic passion with gentle tenderness, and wildness with poetry.

Writing erotic letters and erotic poetry is a good way to start. You can practice your writing with your romantic fantasies. They can be strictly poetic or they can be hot sex, and possibly a blend of both. But writing will get you used to what you will be saying at other times, and writing is an easier way to start.

As an adventure, you may wish to invite your lover to have a sexual correspondence. Invite with your first poem (not necessarily a rhyming poem). If you live together, and one of you gets home earlier, that's even better. It will be a zesty form of foreplay, and if you are physically separated and emotionally bonded, it will be a non-ordinary form of closeness. How many lovers are separated by the miles, relying only on telephones and letters? Make them count. Be daring enough to share yourself and your sexual fantasies on paper and on the phone. I believe those letters will not be tossed. However, make certain you don't compromise your lover in any way. You have to feel safe to be real. And so does he.

Erotic poetry and prose can be enchanting. It is not common knowledge, but Pushkin wrote some very erotic poetry. Now, that's not too shabby. So take his lead and write your own.

I wrote an erotic fantasy, just to myself, to practice saying what was forbidden by my society. I read it over and over again verbally just to get used to saying the words without fear. Believe me, there was a lot of fear when I first read it aloud. I finally got the nerve to read it to someone. This was about five years ago. I never tossed it, and yet I'm still occasionally uncomfortable thinking someone may find it in my desk drawer. The fear society breeds in us goes deep. Even if you throw the lusty prose or poetry away, you will have expanded your boundaries enough to try it again. Don't be ashamed. Shame and guilt are tools of a frightened society. Don't use antiquated tools. They stifle your creativity, and sexuality is a great inspiration for creativity.

After writing erotic poetry for awhile—and remember, it doesn't have to rhyme, but just flow naturally—you are ready to try a letter. Even if you never send it. Challenge yourself. Be erotically creative. No one need ever see it. Use whatever words you wish to use in the context of the fantasy you feel—what you would do to your lover if you had him or her right here, right now. Or, project yourself into another scene in space and time. What do you want to do to him or her—how do you want to do it? Write it all down, and be as sensual and luscious and wet and wild as you possibly can. It truly takes practice, and at first it is terribly uncomfortable. If it comes easily, you're lucky. It took me awhile before I could be comfortable with it. At first I felt even perverse. Now, five years later, I can't imagine having had the discomfort I felt then. You must become totally comfortable with writing before you can go onto speaking.

Speaking erotically is even more scary. So practice writing it first, then read it aloud to yourself over and over until it not so charged with judgment. Allow yourself to get aroused. If it doesn't seem erotic, you might be inhibiting your honest feelings.

You should become comfortable with your feelings. It is your right to know yourself. Read it until you feel really pleased with what you wrote. Edit it if you want. Rewrite it. Fuss over it to make it just right, then read it to someone you trust. A good friend–male or female. Feedback will likely be positive, if you choose the right friend. If it isn't, you chose the wrong friend. Try another one. Then tell your lover what you did. I know he or she will coax it out of you, and it will be a new color on your canvas. The door is now open to a new sexual room in your painting.

Your lover will probably encourage you to write more or to talk erotically during sex. Again, you can send letters and poetry with permission, making sure the letters cannot possibly fall into the wrong hands. In all cases without exception, keep it strictly off the office computer and out of office mail. It cannot be emphasized too strongly, don't ever compromise a person in any way. Privacy can easily be invaded by maliciously oriented or nosy persons, even with special access codes.

Perhaps because it seems so forbidden, verbal fantasies are even more exciting, whether they are on the phone or in the bedroom. Being in person allows for dialog, which your poetic letter could not afford. Now it is mutually expressive. Now the path on your painting shows a couple, hand-in-hand, walking out and into a new painting.

Be creative, joyful and free. If you are having sex on the phone, allow yourself to sexually stimulate yourself physically so that eventually you will become comfortable enough and excited enough to reach orgasm. This type of mutual orgastic pleasure is so satisfying it is exhausting. If you don't feel comfortable going that far, stay within your comfort zone, but stretch yourself a little farther each time.

A word to the wise–make sure your fantasies are compatible. My husband started a verbal fantasy about another woman – a friend of ours – and it totally turned me off. Fantasizing about your partner is much more of a compliment. In any case, realize your act is a loving act of sharing as well as hot sex. Do be considerate, sometimes leading yourself and other times allowing your partner to lead you into a mutually created fantasy where you both are creating the scene and action. This is sexual communication, and the operative word here is 'communication'.

The more often you do this, the easier and more enjoyable it will become, and the more poetic you will get. Just like giving oral sex, the more often you do anything, with conscious but natural attention, the better you get.

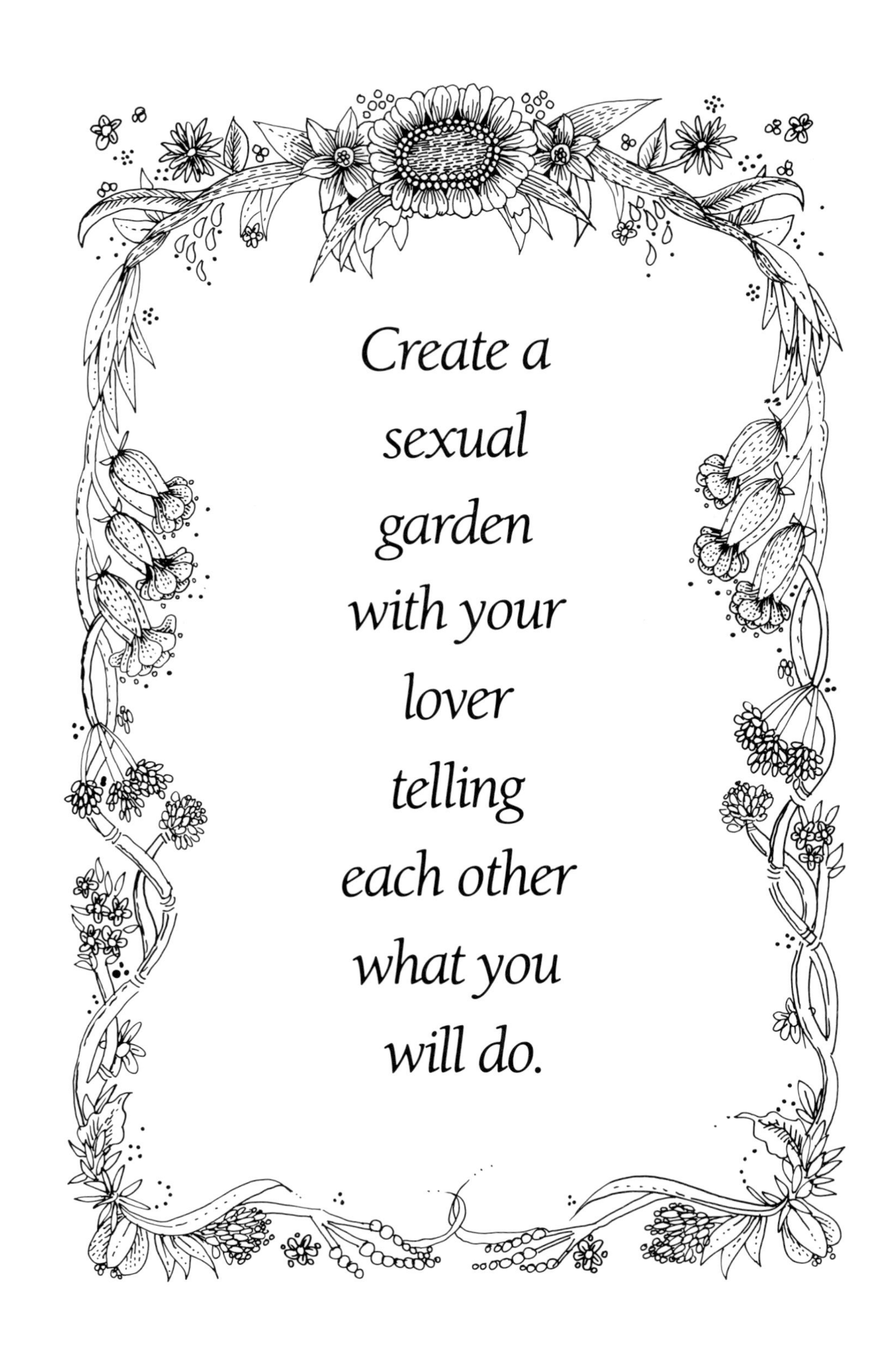

Create a sexual garden with your lover telling each other what you will do.

Magic Beyond Space and Time

Sexuality is an interesting phenomenon. It is something that can be experienced on many levels. It can be purely an exciting exchange of energy, an enhancement of one's vitality, an animal expression of passion, or an interchange that enhances connectedness. And it can be all of these at once. It can also, in a certain magical moment, be instantly transmuted into an experience of extreme spirituality, which can then lead one beyond the body, beyond all limits of physicalness, into a space of timeless bliss. This bliss is our human way of experiencing divine vision behind the door of time. It is our mindlink to eternity.

These are moments of the Eternal Now, when the boundaries of our space/time continuum are transcended. These are the moments when our spirit is released beyond the physical, and our bodyboundary is extended throughout the universe, realizing what physicists have known for years—that reality is nonlocal. This means that your atoms are connected to every other particle in the universe, and are in direct communication with the whole.

Although these moments last in time so briefly, the experience is total and our security of 'belonging' is sealed.

How can one question immortality after such experience? It is a moment of truth. Self-honesty is realizing one's self. It is realizing that in truth there are no limits or boundaries. There is only the whole viewed through each individual consciousness—our dance of life, which is enlivened, enriched and secured by love. Not money, not power or control. Only love secures. And it is not love as possessiveness. It is love as knowing the whole. It is touching the hand of the Divine in a very real and direct experience.

Because sex is so acutely intense, the spiritual side of sex can get drowned out by the noise of lust. That noise is still an affirmation. Sex has many faces so she won't become boring or meaningless. Sex is seduction. But sex is so complex that she seduces us into universal knowing. Eventually along the path one realizes that one is being tricked into wholeness—that no matter how we roll around in our oils and scents, we end up at the gate of heaven. And heaven is filled with exquisite life, not boredom. Who has not felt or seen the brilliant burst of light exploding during orgasm?

Because we take a long time in the process of growing, different stages of life will reveal different secrets about sex. The secrets are revealed as we become emotionally ready for them. Since everyone is at a different stage of growth, this transcendental occurrence will not be experienced often or by everyone until they are ready for it. It does not make sex unsexy. It is just much more expansive. When it is mutually felt, there is a powerful interchange. It is so very powerful, indeed, it will highly threaten emotionally insecure people. We are all emotionally insecure on occasion at least to a certain extent. However, if you are courageous, you will not run away from these intense feelings. Then, once experienced, it will be like basking in the sun on a beautiful tropical beach. This does not take away from all the other wonderful attributes of sex—it merely adds one more dimension. It adds the dimension of completion, the dimension of wholeness.

If you have ever felt even the touch of this moment and run away, you will understand the awesome power it holds. If you are frightened by this intensity, it will be experienced as 'the other' swallowing you up. Actually, it is not the other. It is the universe. And it isn't swallowing you up—it is embracing you into its wholeness. The next time you start to feel this, go with it instead of shutting down. Your partner is not trying to swallow you.

Your partner is feeling the same encompassing pull; however, in a very real way it is transpersonal. It is the universe become itself through your consciousness. If you feel faceless, without uniqueness, without personality, you are. For these moments you are the universe in love with itself, becoming itself within your embrace. Allow that to happen without fear, and you will find a shearing in the fabric of ordinary reality, and a blossoming and revitalization of your unquenchable spirit. You will be revived in your energy, your courage, and your gusto for life.

And in the moments after such sex when you gently and softly reconvene, bit by atomic bit, you heal, revitalize and renew. Don't hasten your return to reality. These are precious healing moments when your entire physical system is being balanced, toned and redirected. Coming back too quickly, because of nervous mind chattering or insecurity or mental fears, will prevent your nervous system from completing its job. For it in fact has a job now. Each molecule of your physical body is touched by this healing energy, by this enlivening, bioelectric, bioenergic process.

If you are afraid each time you release control, of yourself or of a situation, that you are out of control or in the control of another, you will sacrifice this healing and many other magnificent experiences in life. Experience quietude. Practice it. It's well worth it. By devoting time to yourself for growth and pleasure and re-creation through sex, you can gain your freedom. You can gradually learn to give up old fears which may have served you in the past, but are no longer necessary in your current life. Releasing the need to control means surrendering to yourself, not to another. Only in surrender is there freedom.

The door of your spirituality can be opened during your sexual bliss.

A Miracle Occurs

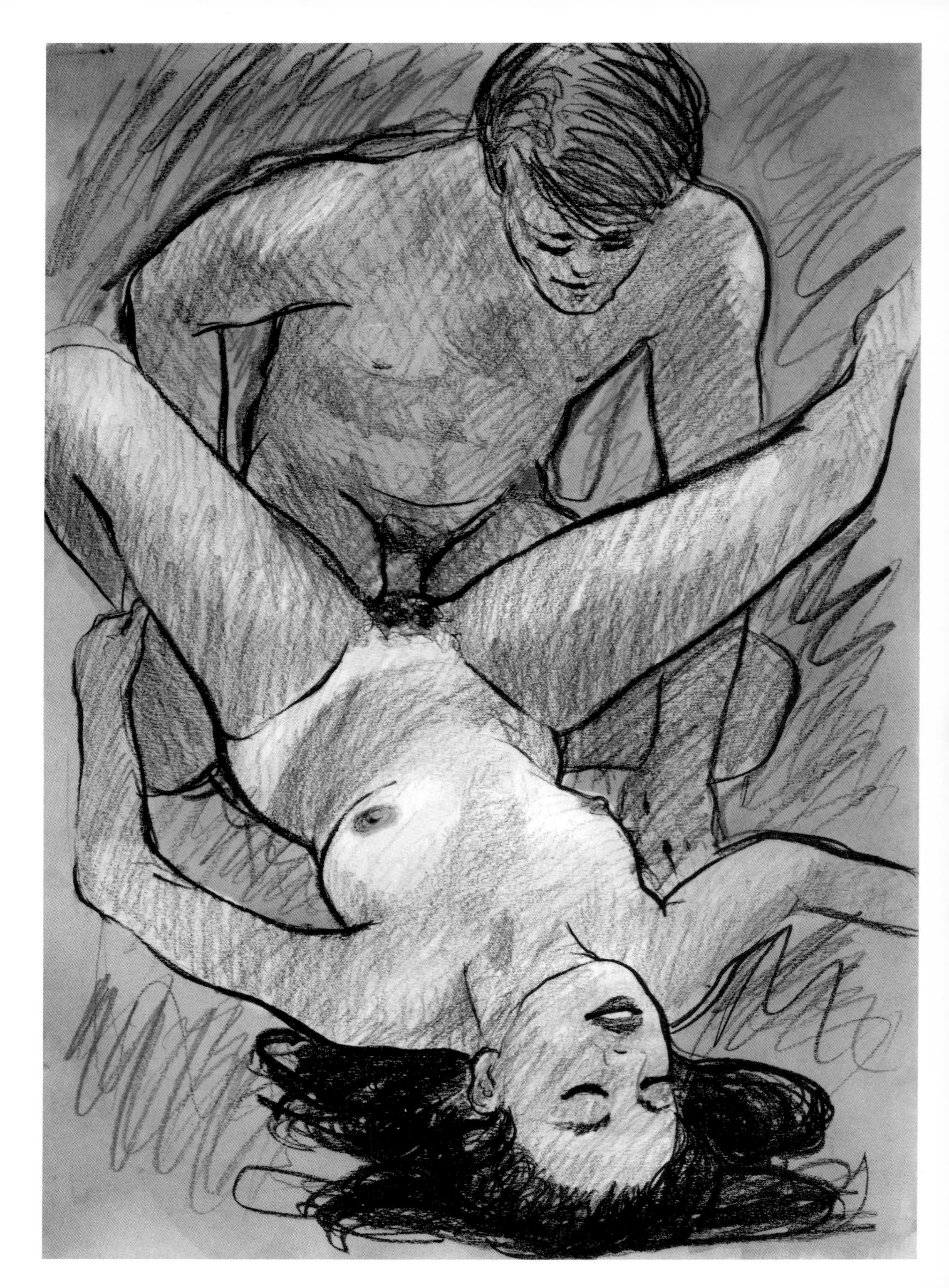

This book would not be complete without speaking of the miracle of sexual intercourse. No matter how many times one has actually entered the other, or been entered by the other, the feeling of a miracle occurring never ceases. There is an absolutely miraculous moment when two bodies merge that is so exquisite, so very special, that nothing can compare, not even another previous time. We can remember it felt wonderful, but cannot remember the feeling itself, for it is a feeling we cannot recapture. We can recapture the longing, but never the actual physical feelings we experience. Maybe that's why we always want to do it again and never seem to tire of the experience.

This is a time when all superficialities of life fall away, when the two persons are actually as the gods in the arms of each other. The primal couple. The only couple in creation. The I-Thou at its most exquisite.

This can be a passionate time or a tender time, or both in a dance of emotion. It is a time when being oneself is paramount, when all pretense dissolves, and the gift of one to the other is supreme.

Of course, it is important to know how to dance. But the two merging bodies have to form the dance in the moment they exist as one. The dance is determined by its own creation. This is a time when power dissolves. No relationship should bring manipulation into this act. Only the power of love itself should reign.

There are many books on position. Many books on technique. Everything you can possibly read about the subject is helpful. But I leave you with this one prime thought: Please never stop appreciating the total miracle involved in the splendor of this special union and communion. Let no one intrude upon your privacy of thought or action.

These moments are yours alone, and should be shared with none other than your partner. It is a non-verbal validation of your life. Appreciate the gift that is life, and the sexuality that has been given you by nature to form such an enchanted coupling of bodies, hearts, souls and minds.

Profaning this act merely makes it ordinary. Strive to keep the miracle of the extraordinary, explicit truth of the human body and heart. On occasion wild passion will strive to grasp hold and keep control, throwing gentleness to the winds. But even that is sacred. This is an act so very special that only poetry or music could touch its domain.

Enjoy your body and the sharing that you have been gifted with, in the way most poetic to your nature.

Follow and experiment with sex manuals, but trust your deepest nature implicitly to create your most personal painting. No one has more knowledge than you. No other is the expert about you and your sex life. You are the artist and the canvas in one. And your personal gallery of paintings is your life's treasure.

In Closing

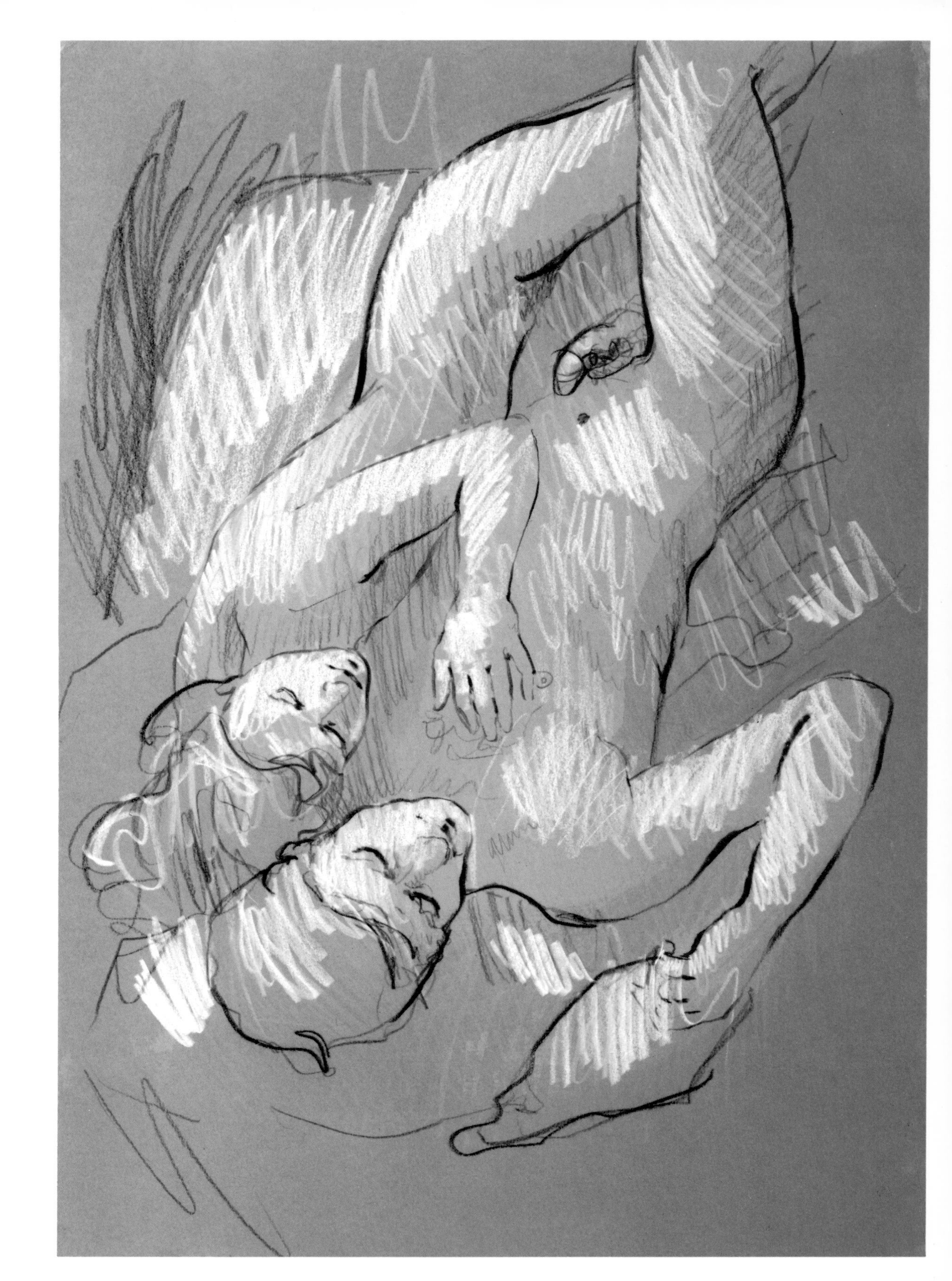

Sexuality at its best is a mystery rather than a series of techniques. The more comfortable you feel with yourself, the more you will be willing to enter that mystery with abandon and discovery. The more emotionally insecure you are, the more your sexuality will seem programmed and uneventful. There is no blame for a poor sex life. A poor sex life means a poverty of your own spirit being unwilling to risk intimacy and discovery. It isn't that your spirit is poor, but that you are impoverishing your spirit. You are delineating it, restricting it, and judging it.

Be kind to yourself. Allow yourself to discover and to have someone else discover you. Allow yourself to feel clumsy. It's a nice feeling of innocence. It's okay to feel a little bumbling if it is from sponaneity rather than because you are judging your performance. Don't be clumsy from judging or being the observer of yourself. Get out of yourself. The other person senses if you are being judging, and will probably take it personally. Just be. Relax. It's okay. It really is. Self-esteem is nothing more than accepting yourself lovingly.

Remember what my muse told me when I asked what sexuality is: "Sex is an erotic painting on the canvas of the spirit." An artist has a spontaneous eye—an eye into his ever-changing spirit. A spirit that needs continual expression to stay alive and creative. Keep that creative spirit growing in your own sex life. Think of sex as a palette of beautiful colors, ever-changing, ever-replenishing. Use the brushes of your creative spirit. Paint all the forms of energy you feel, can feel, and have ever felt. Don't block yourself up with rules and preconceived movements that restrict rather than reveal. You will surprise yourself once you take off the fetters of habit and enter into the beautiful universe of self-expression. I joyfully encourage you to free your mind, free your spirit, and paint, paint, paint!

Sex is an erotic painting on the canvas of the spirit.

Erotic Love Poems

Even now I feel engorged by the memory of our touching
I still can feel my nose caress the soft hair
on your chest and stomach
while my face feels electric against your skin
I taste the haunting perfume of your body
the sense of a natural musk, a slight inviting salt
a tremble of passion, a silk of desire, prolonging sensation
extending time into a long, passionate thread that
weaves through the fabric of our bodies.
How sweet this is.

Before I sleep at night I become very still
It seems as though the air is filled with your presence
and as though, with no boundaries to my soul or body
you waft through the room and me with your gentle presence
And then, other times, I feel a wild passion shake my body
into an immediate orgasm so strong yet so subtle I am amazed
Other times I feel the soft, moist touch of my genitals
and long for your eyes, your lips and tongue to caress me
And when I can't sleep, as hard as I may try
because my trembling body vibrates to your memory and
I slide my fingers onto my tender skin where yours would be
trying so hard to evoke your presence by calling your name
feeling my throat muscles open wishing to slide you into
my mouth and down my throat so you can come into my heart
finally reaching the space beyond reality
where time is merged into eternity
That I am capable of such depth of feeling, there is no doubt
in the goodness of the universe and everything in it.

When I walk, electricity shivers through my body
My shoulders feel hot with energy and my breasts gently throb
with a melting passion that spills down my soft inviting skin
A residue of memory wordlessly caresses my body
I can stand it, yet barely, like reaching the peak of pleasure
just before orgasm and staying on that edge
No boundary to body or time or space, but a merging quality
where the oneness and rhythm of universes
converge in my center
I feel it everywhere – on my skin, in my temporal lobes
in the space inside each atom, vibrating an energy pattern
that is excitement, discovery and joy
I feel sensual to the core of my being
rhythmically throbbing, or feeling what was always there,
just below the threshold of sensory awareness
The subtlty of my passion for you delights me, and as I wait
my soft-skinned labia feels like a delicious erotic fruit
waiting to be tasted and savored by your lips.

I watched you
standing there in the
flickering light
Instead of an interruption
because I was so present
and so alive
your reaching for a condom
was like a ritual
only to lead to a
deeper and deeper level
of joy and discovery.

How can intensity and gentleness be one feeling?
For as intense as I feel, a gentleness weaves through it
to modify and create a new feeling
I am more a part of my environment
and yet less a part of my environment
I'm friendlier to others, yet more distant—but the
distance is not removed from caring but more transpersonal
It's as though I tapped into a great font inside
that I never knew was there
It's attached to eternity
but gets its life and energy in the now
I feel its strength as constant, yet it swells like the ocean
attracted by a full moon, pulling it gently upward
encouraging movement and swelling of greater powers
Yet the moon couldn't be full without its other phases
The tide wouldn't move without the gentle letting go
And the pulsing in my body is so eternally rhythmic that I know
the universe is merely reflecting itself off of me
as its female mirror.

I'm standing at the sink washing my face
but actually I'm recalling what it felt like to
slide my face down onto your gorgeous cock
How gently kissing your thighs led me to such an experience
so unbounded that it was another reality altogether
How you felt in my mouth and throat
How warm and soft your skin was under my hands
How it felt to make you so slippery with my
rich mouth juices that my fingertips and fingers
could ride on and around you so sensually
I love to discover you—your ridges, peaks and valleys
your circular rim
the tender place under and between your legs
so hard beneath the skin
I could delight like this for hours, so slowly
finding your ecstasy and feeling it merge with mine
With each pass through the entrance to my throat
I want to push you deeper, so gradually and sensually
until finally I've taken you all the way in to feel the heat
of your strongest
yet gentlest
passionate
orgastic
flight.

This morning I had such a strong image—
your thighs were before my eyes, my hands
were clasped around the backs of your legs
You were slightly astride, your knees
bent forward, your body tensed
I could feel the hair on your legs
brush my cheeks and lips
You steadied yourself with your right hand
against the wall
Your face fell back, your neck and shoulders tensed
I could hear you gasp, pulling the air
through your clenched teeth
I pulled you closer to my face
breathing in the scent of your skin
feeling my wet mouth slide slowly up your thigh
My right hand slid around to the front of
your thigh closer to my mouth
and as I licked your skin, my fingers
became wet and slippery
Slowly my hand moved around your expectant
and shivering cock and finally
when you felt my grasp
you released your breath
And still moving slowly I pulled you
into my face, firmly, sliding you down my throat
feeling hot, shaking with passion
My left hand moved higher on your thigh
around your buttocks, stroking you sensually
My right hand, now slippery, moving with my mouth
taking you deeper into ecstasy

Time stood still—eternity merged with the cells
of our being, transfixed out of time and space
Slowly, deliberately, consciously
I built with you, higher, more intense
higher yet, more intense yet
At some point a nova—a supernova—of energy occurred
and as I felt your body peak with muscles bursting
through your skin like a carved Michelangelo
perfectly formed in memory as eternal as his marbled poems
I took into my body a part of you most sacred and profound
with awe, spectacular and visionary
We spilt upon the floor with melting bones
in peaceful reverie, entranced and healed,
in a state of mind which only God knows constantly.

I see myself lying on the beach with you
Lying on our backs, talking about life,
Discovering each other palm to palm
as we joke, reveal and speculate
Looking at the stars
appreciating the vastness of it all –
Looking into a clear night sky away from the facade
Always amazes me –
At how we tend to stop movement with our categories
That life is an adventure of movement
at the very basis of our being
That every second stars explode
and galaxies collide in cosmic fireworks
That light is a prime mover and constant energy release.
You roll over onto your side
and gently stroke the side of my cheek
with the back of your finger
and I wonder if the stars have feelings like this.

I looked up into your face
rippled with lines of ecstasy
The lights undulated
reflecting their colors off the ceiling and walls
as though refracting through water
I had no idea the amount of energy
that would fill me when you entered my body
Boundaries disintegrated
Every nerve reverberated with cosmic resonance
beyond the physical so that the physical
melted as a mere pretext to what was real

The real was as intangible as
distance is to non-local connection
In those moments I understood everything.

I held the phone like a teenager
My clothes were off
I grabbed a pillow and
placed it on my abdomen instead of you
I lifted my radiant thighs to my chest
and the empty ceiling
grabbed my feet with my right hand
and splayed out my knees like a happy frog
My whole genital area throbbed with expectation
as your voice reverberated through my core
We talked about everything else
except what was on our minds
just like teenagers
I really wanted to toss the pillow
and feel your strong thighs under my butt
To have you fill me up to my ears
with your body and your passion
and your excitement and daring
with your dreams and aspirations
and with your body
and with your body
and with your body

The fountain is splashing happily
while African drums beat on Michigan Avenue Bridge
Pigeons jump for the scraps
Pre-teens jump the embankment, used to
the built-in playground of Chicago's architecture
Suburbanites revel in the city's joys
unaware of what's making them happy
but enjoying it just the same
Hot breezes so gently touching our faces
Girls and boys everyone
leaving adult faces at home with the
abandoned responsibilities
Couples walking arm over shoulder
hand in hand, smiling, chatting
aware of each other's presence
casually using the city's pleasures
as a backdrop for their romance
Millions of photographs of today's joys
Snap-shot memories to recall the feelings
on gloomy winter days or when the folks are over
or friends share a coffee or beer at home
That day under the sunny red umbrellas
where I sat unnoticed, content
writing poetry and thinking of you
as I enjoyed the drums, sunshine, pigeons and people.

How many times during a day do I feel your sense
wash through my mental and physical bodies
I can't tell the difference between them anymore – my body limit
has expanded beyond the boundaries of physical self
More like a throbbing gently into the environment
with soft edges probing, tickled by the presence of
plants, flowers, birds, sunshine
Everything is an aphrodisiac to me
Breathing the air, liquid on my tongue, clothes touching my skin
The back of my neck and shoulders tingles with life
The small curve of my back where my tight and slender waist
turns the curve of my sensuous hips
My breastline delicately curving into my sensitive white arms
Arms of strength, beauty, love, sexuality, nurture, joy
and celebration of life at its fullest
How they want to wrap around your beautiful chest and strong
curved back and feel the small of your back where it
turns the curve into your muscular, vibrant hips and
incredibly sensual thighs
It drives me crazy to feel this way, but I love it.

An aching a longing a fantasy needing to be actualized
Delicious memory evokes joy and spirited longing
Longing for my lips to caress yours, to feel your
tongue gently proble my lips, my tongue, my soul
I love to merge with your body, with the whole field that is you
To gently pulse with the expansion and contraction that is
movement and change, and then to separate
An energy dance flickers in memory on the ceiling of my thoughts
Turning, swirling, swimming through the field of consciousness
like a mirrored ball over our bodies
Lights flickering in a passionate night
Shooting stars of energy and balance—the duality
of excitement and peace together
The dual expression of energy in its finest state—a paradoxical
state needing freedom to grow to bloom to touch
and then again to separate, always in movement and dance
Without the dance it falls static and lifeless
like a movie that fails to move
Joy needs to dance and curiosity and discovery
are its happiest companions.

MASTER PIECE SEX 170

As we spoke, the air became electric with your energy
I went into another spacial dimension
as my thoughts became words
Slowly the electrical currents blanketed my skin
and I slid between dimensions
Sensations of touching your skin with mine
Feeling your sexual energy
course over my body like a magical surf
breathless, floating in bliss
breathing only to speak
feeling, feeling, feeling
like the slow movement of a deep sea
with magical wonders all around
sunlight flickering above on a gently lapping surface
It was hours, days and years in those moments
a timeless memory of our own creation
a snapshot never to fade
more like a treasure shell taken from the sea
set on a nightstand as an inspiration
to travel farther still to infinite possibilities
beyond the stars or maybe instead
to enter them.

Lying in the warm sand on a blanket in a deserted cove
a world of its own, small lapping peaceful water sounds
no one for miles – no boats, no people, only hours from Istanbul
yet not of this world, I feel your fingers gently lace through mine
and a warm surge of energy rises up my arm
My skin is eroticized by your touch
Warm rays of sunshine speckle the cove and
intermittent shadow plays a gestalt on the sand and our bodies
A little cooler now, you slide your arm over my back
and again a shiver of electricity floods my body
How do you know the way to touch that part of me
so subtle none can see
We roll onto our sides, and I lift my right leg over your left thigh
and pull my body close to feel your erection impinge gently into my
pubic bone – again an electrical charge surges through my senses
We furtively confirm our solitude as I feel your hand
slip a strap down to bare my shoulder and breasts
I feel wildly charged as you slide your hand around my breast
feeling my nipple engorge with pleasure, gasping with awe
feeling enchanted with desire for you – my eyelids flutter with
passion as I feel you pull down my suit and slide yours aside
And again I gasp, feeling my eyes roll up pulling me
higher into your spell
Hopelessly willing, I feel you slide your engorged cock deeply
inside of me – you pause, holding your breath with awe
withdrawing slightly, pressing yet deeper, withdrawing
pressing deeper until the physical has become mental and the mental
has become spirit, and flying together in some cosmic bliss
we pass through a series of successive gates in paradise
each with a new splendor and level of awareness
By now we take our turn looking at the stars, and

no longer is the lapping water apparent in our consciousness
Interlocking fingers we fly through eternity
experiencing in these moments meaning without words
creation of joy without object, a bliss given freely
to acknowledge life and say... thank you.

I hardly remember hanging up the phone
Your voice was still in my ears, your touch still on my skin
I slid my hand between my soft-skinned thighs
I was moist, slippery with passion thinking about you
I felt you inside of me, sliding deeper
with gentle, firm, penetrating strokes
I shivered, cried, extended my breasts, arched my back
I kept feeling you penetrate, withdraw
penetrating vibrance, energy, joy
I cried out your name into the dimension where
you hear me no matter where I am
I felt you totally encompass me in the space where
I can always be reached, touched, tasted, embraced
Higher yet, stronger, tighter, wilder
more passionate, hotter
until you finally threw me from the heights of passion
into paradise where I floated and where I awoke in the morning
sprawled out on the warm sands of memory.

Too close to focus, I look down your nose to see your soft
sensual mouth – my thighs are around yours
I sit astride your legs, feeling the moistness between my thighs
My hand slides around the back of your neck as your body sighs
and leans backward against the sofa, relieved to be touched
bathed in feelings of sensuality and emotion
Lights flicker on the walls and ceiling making a dizzying feeling
A candle flickers, dancing its own dance of feeling and wonder
I gently run the back of my finger across your soft lips
They part and you gently stop my finger with your teeth
I lean into you with my warm and soft breasts, heart pounding
swirling blood and emotion through my veins so hot for you
so deliciously melting from your touch as you
slide your hand around my curved waist
We hardly breathe and yet that is the only sound
My lips touch your cheek, eyes, forehead and I feel you respond
pulling in your breath with bliss
breathing the electricity of your body rather than the air
as you put your face into my breasts and breath them into
your awareness – that cosmic awareness of knowingness
I can't move, stunned with feeling as your lips softly encompass
my nipple – I gasp in a breath and again am aware of the
wetness of anticipation between my thighs
We squirm into each other, tighter, so close our skin merges scent
And as you lift me with your strong hands, I slide mine into
your lap, wrapping myself around your hard cock, caressing it
carefully, completely, with wonder and excitement
Moistening my fingers to slide around you more easily
Feeling your rim, the opening of your sexual body
feeling my own becoming more moist with passion
You lift me gently and I pull up onto my knees, then slide

down on you slowly, slowly, both of us breathless and stunned
by feeling, a moment captured covering aeons of history
the universe captured in this moment
Lifting, lowering, slowly, cupping my hips in your palms
guiding me in the rhythm of your passion
I slide the soles of my feet onto the cushion below us, and with
limber and agile movement increase our passion and rhythm
The lights flicker, reality fades, and instead the world becomes a
flurry of creation bliss, and with our pounding explosive orgasm
another galaxy is formed in another universe of space and time.

You slide
down my sexual body
gracefully
with power
and quiet delight
I feel the pulse
of your energy–
the merging
of our fields
becoming living poetry
How delightful to share
so intimately and deeply
the self becoming
more than self–
the universal vitality
into which
sexual energy emerges.

My lips brush your eyebrows, my fingertips slowly run along
your temples to the back of your neck
Quiet music, light flickering off the walls—so peaceful, so exciting
You breathe in the scent of my skin and slide your hands
around my slender waist
My legs cup your thighs and you lean deeper into the couch
feeling it give way into another dimension of time and space
another reality—the reality that comes only from touching
and being touched
That simplicity of movement becomes grace itself
That rush of blood becomes thrill, always new
always fresh, always healing
I gently lean my soft breasts into your chest and feel you
breathe into me with your heart
I brush your nose and cheek with parted lips
breathing in the essence of you—that superb essence
that surrounds me when I think of you
each time the same perfumed essence that is yours distinctly
I cup your head lightly and you feel a rush of hot energy
engulf your mind
My lips caress your soft earlobe, so sensitive, and you feel
my warm, moist breath, and hear it flow into your mind, and
you know I'm making love to your mind and caressing your soul
I lift my torso trembling involuntarily as my energy
rarifies and expands
My whole center is a golden column of radiant energy
pulsing through my body, coming through my skin and
filling the air with perfumed joy and life
I feel light pulse through my arms, merging with yours,
pulsing light, both hot and cool, surging through
my genitals and legs

Time disappears and eternity opens up like an exotic, radiant
flower, and we are the core center, pulsing as the petals open up
feeling hot, joyful, being bliss rather than feeling it
I sense you hot and hard under my opened hips, tight and soft
silkened skin pulsing golden light
radiant energy converging to a focus, hotter, brighter
building higher and higher
Our bodies disappear into a golden pillar of sacred energy
so consuming that the boundaries of I-Thou transmute into
the power of God—pure energy without limit
the energy of unbounded flight
You slip your golden scepter of light into your pulsing hand
as I lift my body to my knees
I'm shaking with passion and desire for you
My fully opened golden flower of sexual passion invites you in
unconditionally, and as I slide my radiant body down slowly
to the base of your cock where it enters your body as well
as mine, you gasp with pure bliss, entering yourself
as well as me, entering the gate of your deepest self
And the splendor of light is all there is at this highest level
this God level—pure light—and it is each of us
We stay at this peak of discovery longer and longer, lingering
and finally explode into universal energy
again creating a galaxy for another universe to enjoy.

I heard your voice on the phone and I was so soothed
The tenor of it is like a sweet oil that balms and heals
Even though you were tired I felt the soft energy of you
caress my spirit and heart, giving me feelings of
peace and excitement comingled
As direct current will burn, the alternating current of
touch-release, touch-release creates most effectivly
Without releasing, touching loses its vibrance
Breathing out is as important as breathing in
Between meals is as crucial as the meal
And in our case, separation is as important as contact
Like the ebbing and flowing of the sea
or the sun and storm of the weather, or playing and working
They all increase definition, and too much of anything
consumes in destruction
The times I don't hear from you are as important to me
as the times when I do
I've thrown away men who endeavor to put me in the
capsule of their need
Maybe that's why priests become a bore, and prostitutes
become sexless with overuse, and relationship is destroyed
because it is thought that constance is normal
that contact is continuous, that feeling is controllable
and control is desirable
Normal is synchronous not monotonous
continuity is not the same as continuous
Strength is not a lock, but flexibility
The integrity of a chain is in its flexibility, which is made of air
as well as metal, or of subtle DNA, linked and not linked
The most fascinating flowers open with the sun and
close with the moon—all nature is cycle and balance

And be pleased that your not phoning is as equally
valuable to me as your phoning
Your soft tones are real and not forced
I can write poetry and not write poetry
I can think of you, and I can forget about you
Only in releasing your memory can I remember you.

Kiss my face
where my nose turns into my cheek
and my cheek turns into my neck
Kiss my neck
where my neck turns into my shoulder
and my shoulder turns into my breast
Kiss my breast
where my breast turns into my torso
and my torso turns into my leg
Kiss my leg
where my leg turns into my thigh
and my thigh turns into my buttocks
where it then turns into my back
and my shoulder
and my neck
and my face
And then please
kiss my eyes
and my lips.

I feel myself on the back of a motorcycle with you
We're riding through the mountains, but it's not cold
My arms are wrapped around your chest and my hands fall low
onto your center, your hara area of power and identity
The scent of the air is beautiful, fresh, alive with life and spirit
Birds sing, fly, chirp in the trees
An occasional hawk dots the sky, soaring a flight pattern
only he understands as he catches the wind
Nowhere is life so beautiful as here
At no time in my life have I been more alive and happy as now
feeling the warm sun play with the cool shade in a dance
only they can share
We turn off the main road onto a service road that leads
to a *cul de sac* of trees and grass
Getting off the bike our ears are still vibrating, but by the time
our blanket is down with grapes, bread, some cheese and
sweetened nuts, no helmets and only silence, we breathe quietly,
smelling the myriad scents and appreciating this beauty
You pass the canteen to me—the water is warm
with a touch of lemon that tickles my mouth
You unwrap our feast, spread some sweet cheese
onto a heel of bread and offer it—
Such a simple gift, but like all of life, the simple is the sweetest
Preparing your own, I wait, and watch your strong tanned arms
and sensual hands move a knife across the bread
We taste each bite, the smooth creamy cheese
the crisp edge of bread, the soft center so French
Tired, you slide down onto your side to relax after you've
swallowed the last bite of your morsel of bread and cheese

I too slide down to my side with a small handful of grapes
facing you. As you close your eyes I place a grape to your
soft lips and your mouth releases to accept the sensual offering
Biting down gently, the center wets your tongue
Again a simple gift
We roll onto our backs and sigh with the pleasure of the woods
Even the ants seem to be napping
Eyes closed, we see leafy shadows flicker across our lids
You reach for my hand, and I feel your warm fingers
lace through mine which are cool
We enter a state of mind where all is right with the world
Peaceful waves of energy pulse through our bodies
with each heartbeat as our breathing slowly synchronizes
and our bodies sink deeper into relaxation
With shoes holding down the four corners of our blanket
we feel our toes caressed by the cool air
Touching only with fingertips and spirit, we drift
in and out of clouds, boundaries of body melting into bliss
An hour becomes an oasis of joy and peace
Renewed and refreshed, we hop back onto our metal stallion
blazing the trail that leads to the next oasis to the next road
to the next oasis in a dance of life and spirit
like the touch and withdrawal of a kiss
Kiss me to remind me
I never wish to forget how I feel when you touch me or
how I feel when I breathe the air of lovely scenes as this.